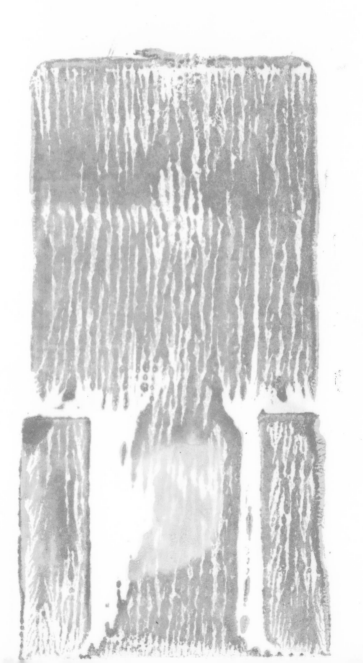

Homage
to
GALILEO

Homage
to
GALILEO

Papers presented at the Galileo Quadricentennial
University of Rochester
October 8 and 9, 1964

Morton F. Kaplon, *Editor*

THE M. I. T. PRESS

Massachusetts Institute of Technology
Cambridge, Massachusetts, and London, England

CONTENTS

v

LIST OF CONTRIBUTORS

Philip H. Abelson	Editor of *Science*; Director, Geophysical Laboratory, Carnegie Institution of Washington.
Gilberto Bernardini	Director, Scuola Normale Superiore, Pisa.
Georgio de Santillana	Professor of History and Philosophy of Science, Massachusetts Institute of Technology.
Norwood Russell Hanson	Professor of Philosophy, Yale University.
Erich Kahler	Distinguished Scholar, Foreign and Comparative Literature; formerly Visiting Professor, Cornell University, Ohio State University, Princeton University, University of Manchester, Institute for Advanced Study.
Morton F. Kaplon	Chairman, Department of Physics and Astronomy, University of Rochester.
Edward W. Strong	Professor of Philosophy, University of California at Berkeley.

INTRODUCTION

GALILEO GALILEI (1564-1642) was a unique intellect—mathematician, physicist, astronomer; he is often referred to as the father of modern scientific thought. His contributions have made a lasting impact on modern society, and his life and the controversies concerned with certain aspects of it hold many parallels for us today. In reading about Galileo, I was reminded of a comment by Professor E. Schrödinger in his monograph entitled "Statistical Thermodynamics." He states, in commenting on the behavior of a degenerate gas, that a certain result is "at once (a) satisfactory, (b) disappointing, (c) astonishing. . . ." Galileo's numerous contributions are certainly most satisfactory, but he is disappointing in what he failed to do and astonishing in the depth and breadth of his discoveries.

Each fall, the University of Rochester holds an all-university convocation. For the occasion of the 1964 Fall Convocation, President W. A. Wallis suggested it would be particularly appropriate to focus on Galileo on the occasion of his four hundredth anniversary and to attempt a considered re-evaluation of his contributions in the context of our present society. At that time, a serious re-evaluation of the role of modern science was currently topical and is still controversial. The parallels were many. Galileo was one of the first scholars to recognize the need to disseminate scientific knowledge to the public and to write in the public language; the lack of a broad-based understanding of the role of scientific progress and its effect on society is still a critical problem today. We are still arguing the basic question of the right and need of free inquiry without restrictions. Who should be supported, to what extent, and is it necessary? There is the problem of breaking with established tradition: for Galileo, the Aristotelian heritage; for us, the almost unbroken "inner circle" of advisers, and so on.

The program evolved to a format focusing on individual papers, each followed by a discussion of the topic presented. It was clearly impossible in a limited time even to attempt a considered coverage of the vast scope of Galileo's contributions and his impact; we thus defined the contributions in an attempt to highlight three aspects. The six papers presented in this *Homage to Galileo* represent the papers presented by our principal speakers and may be separated into three categories.

The first category, represented by the papers of Professors de Santillana and Bernardini, is characterized by their consideration of Galileo's heritage for the present. The second is more concerned with inquiry into specific aspects of Galileo's scientific work and is represented by the papers of Professors Hanson and Strong. The third category reflects the larger problems of the interaction of science with other major aspects of society. To a large extent it is rooted in the Galilean heritage, without which many of the problems we are currently facing would probably have been somewhat delayed in their arrival; this area is represented by the contributions of Dr. Abelson and Professor Kahler.

In presenting the papers we have attempted to retain the flavor of their oral presentation and have introduced minimal editing. In this respect it is worth noting that Professor Bernardini gave his address on the occasion of the formal Convocation, at which time he received the honorary degree of Doctor of Science. We regret that it is impossible to present here the vigorous discussions which followed each of the papers. There may well be objections to our selection of viewpoints and particularly to those which are entirely missing. I refer to the controversy, still extant, over the relations between Galileo and the Church and the "other" side of the controversy. However, this is a *Homage to Galileo,* and his stature is sufficiently high that a little leavening may never be noticed.

The working physicist takes quite a few things for granted. He certainly knows that Galileo played an important role in the development of the concept of inertia, that Newton formulated the basic laws of classical mechanics as we now know them, that Einstein rethought the fundamental problems concerned with the nature of space and time and so on, but he has little feeling for the real flavor of the historical development of the subject. How many know that Newton thought his greatest contributions were in theology or that Hamilton believed quaternions would be to his and Ireland's lasting glory? Galileo was more perceptive. What difference does it make if one knows little of the history of ideas? If the answer is unclear, this selection may help in arriving at a new understanding. If this interest exists, one will appreciate even more the scope and depth of Galileo. Professor de Santillana says in his introductory paper, "Galileo has by now moved out of history into myth. He is more than the creator of an era. He has become a hero of civilization, the symbol of a great adventure like Prometheus, or rather like the Ulysses of Dante and Tennyson." Professor Hanson begins by stating, "Giants are frightening at close range.

Introduction

One views them with detachment only from far off." While Dr. Abelson says, "Galileo's contributions were not only in the discoveries he made, but equally in his procedures in making them and in later working for their acceptance. In effect, Galileo discovered science."

If Galileo is but a name in history, it is our hope that this selection will help in discovering him; if he is already known, that it will expand even more the appreciation of his contributions; and, in either event, that this may lead to further inquiry into the individuals and their ideas from which our modern society has evolved.

It is a difficult task to acknowledge adequately the many individuals and organizations who have contributed to the development of the program. Particular thanks are due the National Science Foundation, which contributed in a major way to the support of the program. Professors Lewis Beck, Robert Marshak, Colin Turbayne, and Hayden White and Dean Kenneth Clark contributed significantly to the concept and development of the theme of the celebration. To all of these, we express our appreciation.

MORTON F. KAPLON

University of Rochester
Rochester, New York
September, 1965

Homage
to
GALILEO

GIORGIO DE SANTILLANA

GALILEO IN THE PRESENT

Galileo has by now moved out of history into myth. He is more than the creator of an era. He has become a hero of civilization, the symbol of a great adventure like Prometheus, or rather like the Ulysses of Dante and Tennyson.

There was in his earlier triumph the note of divine surprise, of an incredible world opening up. There also is, later, darkness closing in on the hero. Let me quote a famous letter of his to Diodati from 1638:

> Alas, honoured Sir, Galileo, your dear friend and servant, has become by now irremediably blind. Your Honour may understand in what affliction I find myself, as I consider how *that* heaven, that world, that universe, that by my observations and clear demonstrations I had amplified a hundred and a thousand times over what had been seen and known by the learned of all past centuries, has now shrunk for me to the space occupied by my person.

"That heaven, that world, that universe." This has the epic ring, the love for the discovery of creation, that would well have befitted the Argonauts' enterprise, where modesty would hardly have been fitting. At this point, already the prisoner of darkness, compelled to silence, Galileo goes on with the temper of a heroic heart, re-examining, reorganizing, reshaping without cease the vast array of his ideas in a creative impulse which leads him to his most powerful achievement, the *Discourses on Two New Sciences.*

He was establishing the foundations of dynamics, inflexibly bent on the same enterprise that his judges could not stop, short of killing him. Indeed, his judges, having humiliated him and debarred him from his main object, had no further concern, incapable as they were of realizing that all science is one and that it will break forth again at any point.

"In this way" — writes Galileo to his dear old friar friend, Fulgenzio Micanzio — "I carry on in my darkness, wondering and dreaming over this or that effect of nature, and I cannot quiet my restless brain which keeps me through the night in tormenting wakefulness." We cannot but be reminded here of the Ulysses of Dante, who carries on forever with his great dream even in the darkness of Hell.

It is not perchance that Galileo has always remained at the core of a great dramatic situation. What more dramatic event than the onset of the greatest revolution in history, than this opening up of thought to the idea of infinity — this soaring off on the powerful wings of mathematics, as Galileo once wrote? The magic circle of a closed world centered on man was broken, and it did not go without alarm and distress among many. In the words of a worthy bishop, there was at the time "an universal Exclamation of the world's Decline and approximation to its Period." But if such was a widespread feeling among the learned, all the more admirable to us is the reckless plunging ahead of the great creative minds. "Oh Nicholas Copernicus," Galileo once wrote, "what must have been thy joy in seeing thy thought confirmed despite so many contrary appearances in nature, and all the learning of past ages." It is this joy that we feel in Kepler announcing his new harmonies, in Galileo's lighthearted bantering and his cutting disregard of the powers leagued against him — even in Bruno's overreaching "heroic frenzies."

Those men felt no reason to be afraid for their souls. As Galileo said, why should we be called innovators and trouble-makers, if what we have been able to prove demonstratively belongs to God's eternal truths, that only the ignorance of men could have obscured? There was no fear in the souls of Galileo's own Church friends — those who were able to understand him — but a serene happiness worthy of old medieval Christianity, for they were sure that no discovery of God's works could threaten God's Word, but rather enhance it. The "new philosophy," far from putting all in doubt, was a vividly affirmative one and full of great hope. No one had experienced yet the raw reality of what we call progress. Much rather, science had come in to check that strange feeling of decline, of impending social chaos, that we see coexisting so strangely in John Donne together with a disturbed awareness of the new discoveries.

Even more — Galileo discarded the robed Latin of learning and went straight to the people, writing for them in the vernacular, trusting in all those, he said, who had eyes to see and minds to understand.

His thinking is as straight and limpid as his new style. He has concentrated on the problem of motion as providing an essential clue to the mystery of nature and the real decision between Aristotle and Copernicus — which Copernicus himself had not been able to provide. For cosmology always comes first in Galileo's mind. He has chosen the burning issue. The thought of a sphere turning on itself in a void with no reason to stop — a typical Gedanken experiment — gives him the idea of inertia. And why should this not be the earth itself? Then come twenty years of search leading to the laws of fall, which show motion to be subject to mathe-

3

matics — the great issue is resolved in Galileo's mind. Not quality, but quantity, rules. Now if the moon can be thought of as moving by the same law which controls the projected stone — and the earth too — namely, inertia, then they are no different in nature from the earthly missile. The earth loses its privileged unique condition and is found to be "in heaven " too. The earth *is a star*. The great prophetic Pythagorean word has fallen. When the discovery of the telescope showed the moon to be made of ordinary rock, the circle of proof was concluded in his mind. The distinction between heavenly and earthly conditions is wiped out; the Aristotelian architecture of the universe has fallen. But this time he has proved his case — not only by the telescope but also by the laws of dynamics he has discovered, founded on the new concepts of Galilean *relativity, inertial mass, momentum, instant velocity, acceleration*. Or at least he feels he has, even without Newton — quite enough for a scientific imagination.

He is ready to face the dramatic issue.

It has now become a commonplace to consider Pope Urban VIII and his court as the oppressors of science who jailed and silenced its first representative. It would be perhaps more correct to see them as ordinary administrators surprised by events beyond their ken. They had come into collision with a new force which they could not evaluate. Both sides, the Pope and Galileo, were profoundly bewildered by their unexpected collision. Galileo could not understand that "they" should not grasp the new power of mathematical physics that he was offering them and walked into his trial still refusing to believe that his judges should prove, as he said, "immovable and unpersuadable." *They*, on the other hand, were utterly unaware of the mechanism of scientific discovery, which they could no more stop than issue a writ against an avalanche. In their minds, schooled in the humanistic tradition, they thought they were dealing with *this* particular *Dialogue* — an unique piece of paradoxical ingenuity brought forth by a great writer. They saw it — and Galileo would not have gainsaid it — as a new type of poem. Silence Dante or Virgil, and there would be no *Aeneid*, no *Divine Comedy;* literature would take another course. Excellence meant literary excellence. It could also be suppressed.

As for science and wisdom, why that was another thing. It was in gravity and ponderousness akin to the business of lawyers, which the doctors strove to imitate even in their solemn caps and gowns. It went on forever in the way of disputation and classification, coordinating all things in a vast verbiage without end. It was law and order itself. Confronted with Galileo's dangerous conclusions, the Aristotelian doctor would indeed lose his head and start clamoring, as he does in the *Dialogue:* "This manner of thinking tends to the subversion of all natural philosophy and to the disorder and subversion of heaven and earth and the whole universe!" If Galileo makes gentle fun of this way of identifying his interests with those of the universe as a whole, we still might have a heart for his predicament. Of the heavens, it was understood that man knew little, except their perfection and immutability, a moving image of eternity. They remained inaccessible, it seemed, even with this new gadget, the telescope, for too much had been said about tricky optical effects.

And should we now subvert the vast and documented discourse of the schools — which allows us to account in an orderly manner for nature and life and the soul itself and fits in so handsomely with revealed truth — to launch ourselves in a sea of paradoxes and unnatural conclusions simply because a man has come forward with two lenses in a length of pipe?

It was the professors, and not the clerics, who started the scandal which led to the prohibition of Copernicanism in 1616.

The crisis and the tragedy came later. They have been obscured by so much equivocation that we ought to set the record straight.

Galileo had been authorized by Pope Urban (who had been his friend and protector as Cardinal Barberini) to write a dialogue in which he should examine impartially all the reasons pro and contra the old and the new systems. This was meant by the Pope to be a literary exercise and a further public proof that the question had been maturely weighed before the Church took her decision. For that decision had already fallen twelve years before, in 1616, when it was decreed that the Copernican system ran against both philosophy and Scripture and should be dropped. Still, the Pope now yielded good-naturedly to Galileo's entreaties for a fresh discussion of the problem with the understanding that any system of the universe cannot but remain a pure hypothesis, a "mere" mathematical model. He assumed it was well understood that the actual truth was beyond our reach and that God could have produced the same observable effects in infinitely many ways, for we must not constrain omnipotence within the limits of our particular imagination. In fact, the Pope actually dictated this conclusion in advance and then left his friend Galileo free to display what he was pleased to call his admirable and delectable ingenuity. This has been understood by certain modern positivists as sound scientific prudence *avant la lettre*. It was, of course, nothing of the kind — it was old-fashioned wisdom making sure that nothing should be allowed to disturb it, nor to disturb the approved system of teaching. It was still to be Milton's position forty years later, when he said that God allowed men to conjecture without end,

> Perhaps to move
> his laughter at their quaint opinions wide
> hereafter.

This was the charm of divine philosophy, of God's secrets "to be scanned by them who ought rather admire."

Galileo had to concur respectfully, but, needless to say, his intention was vastly different. He hoped to provide under this proper cover such irresistible proofs of the truth of Copernicanism that the Church would quietly drop its veto and move over to new positions, as it had so often done in the past, in time to be spared an acutely embarrassing predicament. There was thus a deep miscomprehension from the start, what I called a collision course. The manuscript was submitted to the Church censors, examined word for word, and came out with official approval. The censors found it good and full of laudable reverence. The *Dialogue on the Great World Systems* came out in 1632, it was an instant enthusiastic success — and then all at once the authorities realized that they had made a frightful mistake. The usual advisors rushed to tell the Pope that, under pretence of following his instructions, the work was really a demolition charge planted by an expert, that it made a shambles of official teaching, and that it was apt to prove more dangerous to Catholic prestige than Luther and Calvin put together.

Actually, Galileo had deceived no one — except perhaps himself. He had followed instructions, but his persuasiveness had outrun his prudence. He had laid himself open to his enemies by speaking openly. In his work, style and thought go together. The *Dialogue* is and remains a masterpiece of Baroque style, which knows how to move effortlessly through tight passages of reasoning, unroll with a rustle of silk, sparkle with malice and restrained good humor, maintain its cadence through vast reaches of syntactic intricacy, and rise without break to the solemnity of prophetic invective. It was not only ruthless analysis, it was the magic of the Italian language handled by a master, which broke the monopoly of stuffy Latin learning, which took the people into camp and revealed to them the new unimagined power of mathematical physics. Copernicus had remained almost unnoticed, by now half-forgotten. Pascal himself was to state, "It will be a good idea not to go any deeper into the opinion of Copernicus." If that was the policy, it had already failed. Here at last heliocentrism had come into its own.

In his triumph, Galileo could afford to be generous. His scorn and ridicule are only for the silly pedants who had turned Aristotle into a vested interest and were afraid even of looking through the telescope. Aristotle himself, he insisted, would have been the first to come over to his side if he had learned about the new discoveries. And may I quote here something that I have come upon, which Galileo never knew, but which confirms him utterly. It is a passage from Averroes, surely the greatest of Aristotelians, who had lived 400 years before: " In my youth," he says, " I had hoped that the better scrutiny of the heavens that we need would be achieved by me. In my old age now I despair, but I still hope that my words will induce someone to carry on the search." Is it not a way of begging for the telescope, which Galileo was to offer him too late?

The *Dialogue* is thus a work, truly a poem, of reconciliation. Worldly-wise, it remained terribly dangerous.

If anybody was technically at fault, it was the censors who had been unable to understand. But now the Pope's anger flared high, for he realized that Galileo had only tagged on perfunctorily the profound philosophical ideas that *he*, the Pope, had dictated. There is no fury like a philosopher scorned. Urban wanted now to make a resounding example.

Still the law was on Galileo's side. All the Pope could do by rights was punish the censors and have the book prohibited administratively. It was frustrating and infuriating.

At this point the Inquisition "discovered" in the file a heaven-sent forgotten document. That document gave out that *when* Galileo was informed of the anti-Copernican decree in 1616, the Commissary-General of the Inquisition had been present and served a stringent personal injunction on the astronomer to cease and desist from ever discussing it verbally or in writing, in any way whatsoever, under the dire penalties of the Holy Office.

This changed the figure of Galileo from that of a harmless respected consultant to that of a man considered by the Inquisition a special and dangerous suspect and held under surveillance by the thought police. By disregarding the injunction, he had exposed himself to being considered an obdurate heretic, which meant death at the stake. The authorities could try him at last. They now had an airtight case. They could even afford to be lenient and to let Galileo off with a public abjuration and a life sentence, which was further commuted into house arrest.

The trouble is that the famous injunction seems to have been a forgery — a false record carefully planted by the Inquisitors in their secret file in case it might come in handy. It did. Galileo had never dreamed of it, and that explains why he did not ask the Pope for explicit clearance before he raised the dangerous subject again.

The forgery, or rather the plant, has been proved beyond doubt, to my mind, by historical research over a century. The best proof is that when I published the findings in systematic form in 1955, not one authorized voice was raised to contradict me, although a fascinating amount of evasive action has been taken since that time. (I have in my file some strange cases of dialectical teratology.) It might have provided a good occasion to annul at last the old sentence and rehabilitate Galileo, as was done in the case of Joan of Arc, the more so as I had made a good case for pinning down the guilt on a small group of minor officials who had plotted and acted on their own. Pope Urban stood now in the light of history as a chief badly deceived by his subordinates. He was entitled to rehabilitation himself. But the authorities preferred to stand by their ancient decision, as a distinguished cleric recently remarked out of turn, probably because, however faulty juridically, it represented a philosophical decision concerning the *spirit* of modern science from which the Catholic Church still remains unwilling to withdraw. Be that as it may — I would not dare to judge. The reasons on either side are of such majestic import and profound significance for the fate of mankind that we must expect the unresolved tension to last beyond our time. But as far as Galileo went, his personal position remained clear. His recantation, in the civilized language of his times, meant simply that he would not oppose his will to that of his Church and would not separate himself from the communion of the faithful. As for his scientific opinion, it was understood that he would keep it, and in fact he did not refrain from saying so, at considerable risk. What he thought of his judges, he wrote straight and clear:

> I do not hope for any relief, and that is because I have committed no crime. I might hope for and obtain pardon,

if I had erred; for it is to faults that the prince can bring indulgence, whereas against one wrongfully sentenced while he was innocent, it is expedient, in order to put up a show of strict legality, to uphold rigor. . . .

The animosity, which has never abated, shows how much he remains alive and kicking among us to this day. The strangest misrepresentations have found their way even into unsuspecting Protestant sources; witness the writings of Mallet du Pan and Sir David Brewster in the last centuries.

Again, there have come up writers in our own time, acute and modern minds, mark, bound to no confessional obedience, who suddenly saw in Copernicus and Galileo the "sleepwalkers" who moved in to wreck inadvertently the great unity of science and metaphysics which had held our civilization together over many ages. Those writers were inspired, certainly, by a noble cause and by justifiable alarm, but that hardly justifies their attacking Galileo as a vainglorious "intellectual adventurer " who replaced the absence of proof with "effrontery and illusionism," with "an utter disregard for the intelligence of his readers." Still less does it justify their attempted whitewash of the Inquisition proceedings. Clearly the name of the old man is still potent at conjuring the spirit of hatred and confusion.

This appears more significantly in a work that revives the tragedy on the stage: Bertolt Brecht's famous play, where Galileo is made the hero of scientific civilization as a whole, with its awful contradictions, its revolutionary promises, its human weakness, and its sinister power overshadowed by the cloud of Hiroshima. There is no doubt that Brecht also had in mind the Moscow trials, the conflict of the modern intellectual with totalitarian authority, and that what he denounces is the modern alienation of man's conscience. But in the poetic liberties he takes with his subject, Brecht reveals all the more clearly the misunderstandings that so many of us harbor concerning science itself. Galileo is shown as the exponent of cold invincible scientific method, even a materialist, with a mind that could have led the people to emancipation; but he surrendered miserably once he realized where real power lay, and then wept useless tears of regret. There is a grave misconception here, which goes to the very foundations. No one would deny Galileo's down-to-earth capacities, his enjoyment of the sensuous side of life; but what is so terribly wrong with being a *bon vivant*, in favoring "the newer the idea, the older the wine"? There is no doubt, either, that he impatiently dispelled many dreamy, wonderful, and magic aspects of Renaissance imagination by discovering scientific method — the awful art of separation inexorably divides the true from the false. But his real greatness was not in experimenting with weights, it lay in the power of abstract thinking, in the Pythagorean metaphysical faith which throws a bridge across the chasm between the world of the senses and the realm of pure mathematical abstraction.

In his very language, the greatest Italian prose of the times, Galileo spans the centuries. He is not pushing for a novel philosophy, he is reminding his enemies of theirs, which had been the metaphysical Platonism of the Great Middle Ages. In him there lives the ancient ecumenic and conciliar spirit of Christendom with its rights and its freedoms; when he addresses the spiritual rulers, the clauses of submissiveness scarcely veil the power and authority of his speech, which accuses and exhorts with the dignity of the early Fathers. It is he who is going to save Scripture from the incompetence of its guardians. And he solemnly warns: "The greatest detriment for souls would be, if they were to see *proved* a proposition which it is then made a *sin* to believe."

In fact, it was easy to see even in his own times that he stood for all that was sound in established law and custom, whereas the authorities were resorting to political expediency and juridical improvisation, as they had become the unwitting tools of the streamlined, the efficient, and the new. "These" he wrote bitterly, he who had been accused of introducing novelties, "these are the real novelties which have the power of ruining the State and subverting the Commonwealth."

So much should be said, I feel, to disengage the great struggle from the clichés of conventional history, from the "terrible simplifiers," who see in it only the conflict of free thought against obscurantism. It was, from the start, a conflict among the faithful themselves, who disagreed about the correct approach to natural philosophy. On one side were the professors, the administrators, the representatives of ancient tradition, supported by the massive authority of Aristotle, by Greek astronomy itself in its late phase. This was the house that had been built through the centuries, seemingly on rock. On the other were the new minds, who had grasped the possibility that mathematics and physics, hitherto disjoined, should effect an overwhelming conjunction to show us at last a true universe.

They were perforce a minority, but they had the holy fire. Wrote the good and pious friar, Micanzio, to Galileo during the trial: "But what manner of men are these, to whom any good effect, and well-founded in nature, should appear contrary and odious . . . if this were now to prevent you from further work, I shall send to the hundred thousand devils these hypocrites without nature and without God."

Here we have the call to insurrection, the true revolutionary cry — already in the name of "Nature and Nature's God" — which announces the social breakthrough. And indeed today, at four centuries' remove, we know that it *was* a revolution, that the split was never healed.

Some of us may wonder whether we are not reading dramatic upheavals into the past, while reality may have been a sequence of slow and unnoticed alluvial effects. Was not the whole Renaissance, in fact, were not the medieval schools of science, leading up to this? I suggest that it is best to be coldly phenomenological about it. Revolutionary is as revolutionarily does.

Uprisings, *jacqueries,* justified as they may be, are revolts of the slighted or the oppressed; they are not revolutions. It is only when a group of individuals arises in which the community recognizes in some way the right to think legitimately in universal terms that a revolution is on its way. "What is the Third Estate?" said Sieyès. "Nothing. What could it be? Everything. What is it asking to be? Something." This is fair and reasonable, but that "something" has not been granted or taught from above, it is dictated to them by an inner reasoned certainty, and it is that no-longer-disputable certainty which makes all the difference. Here in the French Revolution are men whose philosophy has grown to impose itself, as it does in the calm utterances of the American Declaration of Independence, men who know they can assume responsibility for the whole body social, not only in the running of its affairs, but in its decisions about first and last things. When these decisions sweep even the entrenched opposition off its feet and move it to yield freely its privileges, as on the historic night of August 4th, then we know that a real revolution has taken place. It is the resolute assumption of responsibility which forms the criterion. It was *that,* and not, as is currently said, the empirical approach.

As if *that* had not existed before. Galileo was not alone

in believing what we see by experience. In fact, the scholars of his own time had an exaggerated respect for the raw data of observation and the commonsense physics that goes with those. Let me say more. If there is any dealing with physical nature by trial and error in the Renaissance, it is rather on the side of the magic-mystic materialists and alchemists, of those of the Stoic descendance. It is they who tirelessly push, mix, drop, concoct, distill, extract, combine and separate, operate with fire, with acids, with solvents and coagulants — always in the effort to move qualities around experimentally. In their *furor empiricus* they ask Nature to speak to them through its many names, effects, and "signatures"; whereas Galileo insisted that the "book of nature is written only in mathematical characters" — by which he meant that, out of indubitable premises arising out of number, weight, and measure, we can set the deductive course of our reasoning as geometers do.

More than once Alistair Crombie, one of our most distinguished students of medieval science, has to speak of the strange "irresolution" which acutely characterizes the attitude of medieval scientists, even the most advanced, either in equipping themselves with the proper knowledge of mathematics or in their way of attempting experiment. Pierre Buridan himself does not really hope that nature will provide the conditions for mathematical laws to be fulfilled, "although it *could* happen that they should be realized through the omnipotence of God." In other words, wouldn't it be wonderful — but only a miracle of divine benevolence could free us from the Aristotelian bondage, which emphasizes commonsense. This is exactly the attitude of the submissive traditionalist versus the revolutionary. Yet Buridan is no timid spirit. His work shows him to be a true rationalist, but he has to defer to long-established authority, whose dictates become akin in his mind to the Deposit of the Faith or the divine rights of kings. For two centuries this kind of speculation has been going on without much happening. Even in the most daring nominalists, the world of the scholar is too well-knit, spiritually and conceptually, not to keep dangerous deviations in check. Nicole d'Autricourt is free to suggest atomism as a natural philosophy, but once the chips are down, he has to back out or become a heretic.

Here and there, the scholar can risk bold theorizing, he can intimate, adumbrate, and prophesy; but he must be prepared for an intervention of authority that tells him to drop his playthings and come back to a correct attitude. This intervention did come at last, brutally, with the anti-Copernican decree of 1616. But this time, however, even if alone and abandoned by the scholars in retreat, there was Galileo. He stated in no uncertain terms that in such grave matters of natural philosophy, his authority was fully equal to that of the Church Fathers themselves. This is what I call the assumption of responsibility. Galileo does not hesitate to denounce the authorities for playing irresponsibly with reactionary subversion. The freedoms granted by tradition, he insists, are his protection, the reason that God gave us to understand His laws is on his side. He makes it clear by his attitude that he will not compromise, that he will not retreat, and that he will be heard.

As we know, Galileo could have gone on establishing the formal science of dynamics without all this fuss. He actually did — by the time he was debarred from writing about cosmology. This would be enough to prove that he did not consider his thought the empiricistic outcome of industrial *division of labor* or *advanced technology* or *bookkeeping* or whatever *gadget* it is that amateur sociologists have devised for his rationale. He felt he had to face the central issue: To the well-worked-out cosmos of his predecessors he opposed another cosmology, another way of knowledge, whereby man has to go ahead forever in discovery, trusting Providence that it will not lead him to perdition. This Galileo maintained even when told by the Successor to Peter, the Vicar of Christ, that his doctrine was "pernicious in the most extreme degree." He alone, with very few men of his time, perhaps only Kepler and Castelli, could really know what he was doing. He saw himself not as the depositary of the truth, but as the initiator of an unending march of ever-growing cohorts, of the whole of mankind, towards an ever-vaster vision of truth, ever receding beyond man's horizon. Here is what I consider Galileo's assumption of responsibility for the whole body social in first and last things. It stands with us to this day.

As for the secularization of thought, it is surely a consequence; it is not the one that Galileo had wished. He still stood for a contemplative natural philosophy in the ancient spirit. He was, as Einstein said of himself, a "gläubiger Physiker." And after all the sound and the fury, there is now at last a glimmer of light on the horizon, a hint of peace. I understand a petition has been introduced in the present Ecumenical Council, by French Catholic scientists, suggesting an official rehabilitation of Galileo. The long refusal and the empty words are now at an end. There is some hope for a true reconciliation.

So much for the past.

There is one aspect of Galileo which is undeniably modern and ours. To use the words of Aubrey, "He was a very ingeniose man, and had a very Mechanicall head. He was much for Trying of Experiments. . . ." He was indeed, for he himself invented the idea of Experiment, as opposed to the old notion of Experience. He even had to invent a word for it: he called it "The *Ordeal* of Experience." This involved extracting a straight yes or no out of nature in answer to a clear theoretical question, and not the usual bewildering play of effect and wonders. It puts theory first, as it should, but it provides a way of testing it — to divide the true from the false. This is the ironclad aspect of Galileo's discoveries, which will go on through the aeons.

But, with this, a great revolution is running its course. It is not so much methodology — a much abused and rather empty word — as the close collaboration of science and technique. The very fact of being content with the *how* instead of the *why* implies the attitude of the man who is concerned with knowing *how;* in turn, he is going to deal with nature in order to obtain the desired result. The physicist operates as a technician. And, with Bacon, Galileo was the first who insisted on the role of the arts then called low, vile, sordid, and mechanical in obtaining knowledge. In his famous address to the Venetians, he pointed out that among the men handling machinery in their arsenal, there must come up experts of unparalleled experience and very subtle intelligence. When the scientist puts nature to the "ordeal of experience," he has to appeal to the technician to help him — as his equal. The experiment that *works* is, after all, the only way to check his deductions.

This is the way of modern science, and it implies changes that are no less impressive in the social outlook than in the strictly philosophical. For it is the new team of scientist and technician which, by opening up the cataracts of successful results, has freed science from the initial metaphysical mortgage. The scientist needs no longer the philosopher's guarantee about the soundness of his approach; nor will he underlie the philosopher's strictures. Nothing succeeds like success.

But freedom has its price. The magic catchword "research and development" has turned science in the public mind into a handmaiden of technology. Nor would the scientists make much of a stand, bewildered as they are about their own assumptions, caught again, as one of them said rather tauntingly, in embarrassing epicyclic expedients as they wait for a true theory.

If we still at least believed with a simple faith in mathematic — But do we really, caught as we are in conventions? A recent paper by Eugene Wigner left me wondering. Its title is "Of the unreasonable success of mathematics in dealing with nature." Such a title would have been unthinkable even fifty years ago.

So many basic ideas are gone that we cannot even put our house in order. The split between the two cultures is widening; the unity of culture, of which science was so large a part, is shattered. The theoretical freedom that we needed for dealing with quantum and particle phenomena has given us an arbitrariness in physical thinking which goes at the expense of metaphysical consistency, as Einstein ruefully pointed out. When the empiricist suggests that science is a set of operational rules for changing marks on paper, he is obviously overdoing it. Science cannot but remain the search for some kind of being, however elusive. But when we are willing to suppose anything that will "work," when nothing is too far-fetched to try, we have surrendered choice of thought and entered a phase which has some of the aspects of intellectual nihilism.

In that sense, we are moving at present out of the era that began with Galileo. We are in search of a new philosophy, for success is not enough. And we must hope that it will be found soon, for otherwise we have a grave crisis in civilization. Inevitably, if science were to insist on presenting itself as an assemblage of devices for pragmatic power and economy of thought, if it were to disguise its poetic objectivity under technological wizardry, then misunderstandings would be found to occur. Outsiders — the other culture — will ask whether such a program could not just as well have fitted Renaissance nigromancy, with its system of recipes.

The *vox populi* is hard to discern. But maybe some of it spoke to us through the unexpected voice of Salvador Dali, the other day: "For myself, I like it le best today nuclear microphysics because no understand, myself no understand *no-thing* of these. Is *tremendous* attraction for understand something in this way."

We have come a long way since Voltaire.

Those who believe intransigently in the right of science to lead may find those signs irrelevant. The researcher's business is simply to go ahead. But what is left of tradition has a way of turning against those who disregard it. Words such as epicycles and nigromancy coming up in the historical consciousness make one doubt and wonder. The scientist has ceased taking part in the great dialogue as a cultural being. The little gusts of revolt blowing through society are the kind that the statesman might find worthy of attention. *Forsitan et Priami fuerint quae fata requiras?*

If it be true that we are really moving out of the Galilean era, then perhaps you will bear with me if I have so insistently dwelt on Galileo's metaphysics; they are his mark and the mark of that era. I would even go farther, and say: it is not perchance that science was born in the epoch that first took metaphysical commitment seriously.

This may sound paradoxical, for the Middle Ages are supposed to be *the* age of metaphysics. But it was a very different thing, based on the inscrutable will of God, operating inductively from hints of that absolute will. What the Pope instructed Galileo to do was correctly medieval: "Surrender to the inscrutable, speculate as you like, but do not believe that we can really *know*." When the Pope rose in fury against him, it was not because of his experimental discoveries, surely not. Those discoveries he loved. It was because he spotted the pride of intellect which thinks it can establish a true order deductively.

Let me tell you the story. At one point before the trial, the Pope gave audience to the Florentine Ambassador who had come again to plead desperately for Galileo. " I made free to remark to His Beatitude," reports the Ambassador, "that since God could have made the world in infinitely many ways, it could not be denied that this might be one of those ways, as Il Signor Galileo thought he had discovered." At which the Pope, red in the face and pounding the padded armrest of his pontifical chair, shouted: "We must not impose necessity on God Almighty, do you understand?"

Necessity is indeed the fatal word that marks our science. Where there is mathematical deduction of reality, there is necessity itself, which could not be otherwise. This is what Galileo asserts, powerfully and dangerously, in his Dialogue, where he says that when the mind has deduced a necessary proposition, it perceives it as God himself perceives it. There is, he says, an identity at that point between man's mind and God's. The idea of a necessity that is freedom, of a freedom that is necessity, was present in Galileo's metaphysics and not in the Pope's. That is what Sir Thomas Browne had in mind when he spoke of "that exaltation of Truth, in which, against all passions of prescription and prejudice, this century now prevaileth."

The true rationalist instinct is to believe in the reality of what thought is constructing: the Platonist strain will re-appear perpetually to breed new scandal. Even to believe in two and two makes four as an eternal verity is to project back archetypes on the mind of God to limit his absolute will. This is what Descartes realized, and dodged accordingly. But the sound Pythagorean canon of deduction has been re-established, and mathematical physics is on its way, however meagre the results that it can yet show to the public: it may be a shade heretical, or at least "offensive to pious ears," as they said, but it is what we are agreed to call science.

When the God of Job displays his heralding of prodigies, unicorns, and Leviathans brought forth according to his pleasure, he expects Job to break down in uncomprehending wonder. The modern physicist would take it another way. He would say that the arbitrary will of the Deity is a random noise in the system which prevents us from deriving any predictable statements. We cannot try for a science in those conditions.

But if, according to the pious but unhesitating Pythagorean, the holy Number, which is the fountainhead of all things, is an archetype connatural to the divine mind, then the random noise is cut out: our mind is present across the aeons at the stillness of Creation.

I have been using somewhat fanciful language to indicate what, in technical philosophy, would be the need for a prescriptive link between essence and existence. It becomes central, and clearly expressed, in Descartes and Leibniz. That is why it would be fair to call the seventeenth century not only the age of Victorious Analysis, but also that of metaphysical commitment.

But it would be unfair to think of Galileo as the man who, by setting mathematical physics on its way, taught us to see the world as sheer mechanism. He was providing only a mathematical framework for the cosmos, not a universal explanation. As far as the hidden forces of nature go, he was holding on to the good old Renaissance vitalism. His idea of nature is as different from the Aristotelian caricature taught in the schools as it is from the scant and angular mechanism that Descartes was to introduce a few years later and Newton reluctantly adopt as a basis for his theories. It is not quite biological, for Galileo is essentially a physicist; not mechanical, surely, for the underlying reality is imagined to be a flow of transforming and vivifying energy which should be, in essence, light itself. It is what he does not shy from calling by its proper name, the "Pythagorean philosophy."

As those ancients themselves had done, we see Galileo finding expressive symbols of the unifying power of reason in the creative force of life:

> It seems to me that, if the celestial bodies concur to the generation and alteration of the Earth, they themselves are also of necessity alterable; for otherwise I cannot understand how the application of the Sun and Moon to the Earth to effect production should be any other than to lay a marble statue in the chamber of the bride and from that conjunction to expect children.

He goes even further: he delves with fine sarcasm into the unconscious motives of conventional theories. Those modern demonologists of the psyche, who with true plebeian instinct undermine abstract science as a form of escape from reality, might do worse than consider this first inventor of the psychoanalytic approach as he relies on his physics to lead him toward a loving acceptance of life:

DIALOGUE ON THE GREAT WORLD SYSTEMS,
pp. 68-69

Sagredus: I cannot without great wonder, nay more, disbelief, hear it being attributed to natural bodies as a great honour and perfection that they are impassible, immutable, inalterable, etc.: as, conversely, I hear it esteemed a great imperfection to be alterable, generable, mutable, etc. It is my opinion that the Earth is very noble and admirable by reason of the many and different alterations, mutations, generations, etc., which incessantly occur in it. And if, without being subject to any alteration, it had been all one vast heap of sand, or a mass of jade, or if, since the time of the deluge, the waters freezing which covered it, it had continued an immense globe of crystal, wherein nothing had ever grown, altered, or changed, I should have esteemed it a wretched lump of no benefit to the Universe, a mass of idleness, and in a word superfluous, exactly as if it had never been in Nature. The difference for me would be the same as between a living and a dead creature. I say the same concerning the Moon, Jupiter, and all the other globes of the Universe. The more I delve into the consideration of the vanity of popular discourses, the more empty and simple I find them. What greater folly can be imagined than to call gems, silver, and gold noble and earth and dirt base? For do not these persons consider that, if there were as great a scarcity of earth as there is of jewels and precious metals, there would be no king who would not gladly give a heap of diamonds and rubies and many ingots of gold to purchase only so much earth as would suffice to plant a jessamine in a little pot or to set a tangerine in it, that he might see it sprout, grow up, and bring forth goodly leaves, fragrant flowers, and delicate fruit? It is scarcity and plenty that make things esteemed and despised by the vulgar, who will say that here is a most beautiful diamond, for it resembles a clear water, and yet would not part with it for ten tuns of water. These men who so extol incorruptibility, inalterability, etc., speak thus, I believe, out of the great desire they have to live long and for fear of death, not considering that, if men had been immortal, *they* would not have come into the world. These people deserve to meet with a Medusa's head that would transform them into statues of diamond and jade, that so they might become more perfect than they are.

2

GILBERTO BERNARDINI

GALILEO'S INFLUENCE IN
MODERN SOCIETY

Let me confess, without flourishing words, that I am most deeply affected and very proud of the great honor accorded me by the University of Rochester this evening. Let me also confess that I do not feel I deserve this very high esteem; but the Honorary Degree I have now received is phrased with such words that no later than next week, beautifully framed, it will be hanging in the living room of my house in Tuscany. It will remain there through the years to refresh the memory of these days in Rochester, of the cultivated and cordial hospitality of Mr. Wallis, of the warm expressions of affection of my friends, and altogether the feeling of the deep and strong ties I have with this great country.

In his kind letter of April 16 to me, Mr. Wallis wrote, "We hope that Galileo's contribution to science and civilization of the West, which is generally misunderstood, and vastly underestimated, will be viewed more *realistically* as a result of your appearance here." This message touched me, particularly as it came just as the issue of the weekend review of the *Observer* came out with an article signed by Arthur Koestler. It read, "Il Giojello, at Arcetri, where

(Galileo) spent the last years of his life, stands on a hill, among olive groves overlooking Florence, but its name, the jewel, sounds today sadly ironical. The garden, where he received Milton and a stream of other celebrities, is covered with weeds. . . ." What follows has some trace of witty vulgarity. Then he continued,

> Whether this is intended as a deliberate insult — a kind of *"Clochemerle"* in reverse — I was unable to discover; but it certainly testifies to a lack of reverence of the powers that be toward the memory of the man who, in the words of his one-time admirer, Pope Urban VIII, had "given rise to the greatest scandal throughout Christendom." Its shadow still lingers over the desolate house.
>
> The scandal is one of the historic causes which made post-Renaissance Europe a divided house of faith and reason. Legend has turned Galileo into a martyr of the freedom of thought, Urban into its benighted oppressor, and the conflict into a kind of Greek tragedy ennobled by the stamp of historical inevitability. In fact, it was a clash of temperaments, wantonly provoked and aggravated by unlucky coincidences.

I said that Mr. Wallis' message deeply touched me. I have only just in the past few days had the great pleasure of knowing Mr. Wallis personally. I fully realize now that each word of his kind letter had a specific value, and particularly the words "viewed more realistically." For this reason I do not need to say that I am fully aware that I am unable to fulfill my task.

The conception we usually have of a great man of the past is largely influenced by the historical development which links our ways of being and thinking to him. Surely we can say that the greater the impact he has made on the historical development of civilization, the stronger and deeper these links are made; and it becomes more difficult for us to establish an objective perspective of his personality that may do full justice to his intellectual and moral stature.

Actually, this interaction between him, the great dead man, and us follows some more or less general laws. On the one hand — not very differently from our ancestors who created legends and myths — we like to see in these great men of the past the symbols of some perennial ideals of mankind; on the other, the achievements of these men-gods usually still influence so substantially our daily lives that it is difficult, if not impossible, for us to measure properly their original intrinsic values.

These laws of historical distortion — unavoidable and irreducible as they are — operate particularly where Galileo is concerned.

His dramatic life was quickly framed by legend, but at the same time his fundamental works on mechanics were rapidly diluted by the vigorous growth of this science, of which he was indeed the founder. His language, intentionally addressed to anybody capable of thinking, his warm call to faith in human reason and in the power of human knowledge, became, through the centuries, the banner of intellectual freedom; yet this language is largely our own language of today, this faith, daily supported by countless observable facts and by our understanding of them, is a matter of common consent.

Furthermore, his birth, which the University of Rochester has so solemnly celebrated these days, the fourth centenary, occurred at a time which can be considered particularly favorable to his spiritual qualities, to his intellectual eagerness and fervor. His birth occurred when, on the fertile ground prepared by the Renaissance, the attacks of the French School against Aristotelian physics, the new individualistic approach to the Bible and to Christian doctrine, the Columbus Atlantic venture, were gradually dismantling — on behalf of a new sense of human dignity — the medieval certainty of a fully organized and accomplished world, buttressed by theological and metaphysical principles often tainted with superstition. However, it is not mere chance that his life spanned the dawn of the scientific revolution. A contemporary of Descartes and Kepler, Galileo represents in this triangle the vertex from which the new philosophy sprang most vehemently and with vast consequences. With these considerations in mind, I am fully aware that I am running the risk of increasing, instead of decreasing, the distortion of historical perspective on Galileo by my own personal and professional distortions.

However, physics being the ground on which I move a bit more freely, this is where I will start. Galileo is often called the "Father of Physics"; less frequently, the "first modern physicist."

One may notice the subtle difference between these two designations. I think, however, that they are not quite appropriate in characterizing Galileo's historical significance. He was the "Father of Physics" for the revolutionary trends of his natural philosophy. He is the "first modern physicist" because he first went from a commonsense consideration of natural phenomena — the slow swinging of the pendant lamp or the too-quickly-falling body — to *quantitative* experiments made by constructed pendula or the tilted plane, where respectively the length of the lamp or the acceleration of the body was made large or small at will. He is the "first physicist," not because his name is bound to discoveries comparable to the gravitation law or Maxwell's equations, but because he first expressed the results of systematic observations in mathematical terms and stated that one should try the simplest assumptions in guessing how to describe a new phenomenon in mathematical language. He was the "Father of Physics" because with concrete wisdom and conscious intellectual humility he approached the immensity of nature with these words: "It always seems to me extreme rashness on the part of some when they want to make human abilities the measure of what nature can do. On the contrary, there is not a single effect in nature, even the least that exists, such that the most ingenious theorists can arrive at a complete understanding of it. This vain presumption of understanding everything can have no other basis than never understanding anything."

Let me give evidence for what I have said with a few classical examples. The principle of inertia and mechanical relativity uphold him as the "Father of Physics"; the measurement of time and of the velocity of light recognize him as the "first physicist."

With regard to the principle of inertia, modern scientific thinking is so closely linked to it that it is often hard to realize that it embodies one of the greatest discoveries of science. As so frequently happened with other discoveries, it was formulated over and over again, and Descartes, Huygens, and Newton expressed it in more precise and general terms. But Galileo's discovery differs from most of the others because it was reached by a solitary thinker, who — gradually building for himself a new philosophical approach — found at last the solution to a problem which had been haunting his unique mind for more than forty years.

When a young teacher at Pisa and still almost completely permeated with Aristotelian Natural Philosophy, he posed these questions in his lectures on motion. Two kinds of motion are allowed to a heavy body: a "natural" one when it falls and a "violent" one when it goes against gravity.

What happens when it lies on a horizontal plane and an infinitely small impulsion suffices to move it? What is its motion?

The answer is formulated with increasing clarity in his last and greatest work: *Dialogues Concerning Two New Sciences*. At the beginning of the fourth day, one finds the celebrated statement, "mobile quodam super planum orizontale, omni secluso impedimento, etc. . . .," which synthesizes previous discussions on the problem. Going from Latin to English, the statement is read as follows: "Imagine any particle projected along a horizontal plane without friction; then this particle will move along this same plane with a motion which is uniform and perpetual, provided the plane has no limits. But if the plane is limited, then the moving particle . . . in addition to its previous motion, *which will be uniform and perpetual*, will acquire a downward propensity due to its own weight; so that the resulting motion . . ." Then the answer came to him through the synthesis of two thoughts: first, *imagining* out of the results of a series of experiments what the *reality* would be if the imperfection of instruments and subjective sensations could be surpassed and the phenomenon occur in a world *without friction;* then, figuring out rationally what the motion of a *free body* would be in this world.

Today the motion of a free body is represented by a plane wave, the solution of the free-particle wave equation. One arrives here by starting from the principle of inertia formulated in terms of the relativistic invariance of the energy momentum vector, and then imposing the wave-particle dualism. It is a long way; the two steps in between are Einstein relativity and quantum mechanics, but the philosophical pattern is always the same.

As another example of the extension of this way of thinking in modern physics, let me consider the concept of *anti-matter*. Also in this case we are essentially overriding our more anthropological sensations. For the principle of inertia, it is necessary to imagine a world with no friction — a world where our hands will not be capable of catching anything, where it would be impossible to move around with our legs, to slow down any motion with brakes, etc. In conceiving the antimatter world, the main step, as shown by Feynman, is the *inversion of time*. This is a very hard concept for us to grasp, animals as we are. Life means irreversible time, and while for an animal used to walking back and forth the conception of inverting motion and space is quite easy, the idea of growing younger again is completely beyond our perception.

On the principle of relativity there is no need to insist. These are Galileo's words:

> Closet yourself with some friends in the largest quarters that can be found under the hatches of some big ship and see that you have ... small winged animals, etc. ...: let there be also a small bucket suspended high above another vase with a small opening so that water may drip slowly from the higher into the lower basin and, as the boat *stands still*, observe attentively how the winged animals dart to and fro within the room in all directions ... the drops fall into the basin underneath. ...
>
> Have then *the ship move* as fast as you will and (*so long as the motion is uniform* and not rocking this way and that) you will not notice the slightest alteration in all the above described effects, nor will you be able to understand through any of them whether the ship moves or stands still.

I chose these examples for their peculiar significance, but in the lectures of these past two days, and particularly in those delivered by Professors Strong and Hanson, you have heard already that there are many examples, all characterized by the same type of understanding of natural phenomena. What this "understanding" means can be summed up as follows: *Scientific reality, the only one scientifically acceptable*, is made up of rational schemes which represent the results of all the experiments and observations that could be made, *assuming* that there exist no impediments — *"omni secluso impedimento"* — due to the imperfection of our senses and instruments. The doubt cast by these imperfections is *quantitatively* dominated by the laws of error, of which Gauss gave us the first synthesis, and as I learned from Mr. Wallis, Galileo, the first example. I want to add, as a complementary remark, that this natural philosophy, so clear and valid to any physicist — let me say it for purposes of professional education — has through the centuries offered matter for debate to philosophers.

While Comte and Mach considered it the origin of Positivism, Kant and Whewell saw in Galileo mainly a theoretician who was the first to introduce into science the concept of ideal experiments asymptotically derived from the rational interpretation of phenomena.

Others, impressed by the technological developments originating in the great scientific achievements of the eighteenth century, go so far as to consider him a precursor of materialism. The way to explain these quite different — and often contradictory — views may be found if we focus our attention on some of Galileo's many passages concerning the meaning and value of "experiments." In these passages, we clearly see the transition from a first experiment, with all its inherent errors and misleading appearances, to the interpretation of it; and *then* the *return* to the new experiments to see whether the guess that has been made was right or wrong, whether the presumption of the human mind — wanting to give a rational interpretation to facts — was well justified or not. We know that this procedure simply means to build, fragment after fragment, the Edifice of Science.

Let us now try to view Galileo, the "first physicist," through examples of the measurement of time and the velocity of light. I use again a few fragments of the *Dialogues Concerning Two New Sciences*, quite significant in many other respects. "The experiment made to ascertain whether two bodies differing in weight will fall from a given height with the same speed, offers some difficulty; because ... the retarding effect of the medium. If the height be small, one may well doubt whether there is any difference, and if there be a difference, it will be unappreciable. It occurred to me therefore to repeat many times the fall through a small height in such a way that I might accumulate all those small intervals of time that elapse between the arrival of the heavy and light bodies respectively, so that summing up, one gets an interval of time which is not only observable, but measurable." Ten pages after, he introduces the pendulum. In another section of the book, while describing experiments on the motion along inclined planes, he says, "For the measurement of time, we employed a large vessel of water placed in an elevated position; to the bottom of this vessel was soldered a pipe of small diameter giving a thin jet of water, which we collected in a small glass ... the water thus collected was weighed, after each descent, on a very accurate balance. ..."

There is something more: Galileo introduced time as a normal coordinate. In his diagrams he drew a straight line as the time axis on which he marked time intervals from a zero point chosen at will. Today everybody carries a watch, reads time-space diagrams, etc.; but three centuries ago, time was only the correlation between the cyclic conception of day and night, of moons and years, and the unresting evolution that brings everything but human souls to an end.

Let us now see how he used this concept of measurable short times in one experiment concerning the velocity of light. The experiment is described on the first day of the two sciences. *Salviati speaks:* "Let each of two persons take ... a lantern ... such that by interposition of the hand, the one can shut off or admit the light to the vision of the other. Next, let them stand opposite each other at a distance of a few feet and practice until they reach such skill ... that the instant one sees the light of his companion, he will uncover his own. .... Having acquired skill at this short distance, let the two experimenters, equipped as before, take up positions separated by a distance of two or three miles, and let them perform the same experiment at night. ... If the experiment is to be made at still greater distances, say eight or ten miles, telescopes may be employed." *Sagredo remarks:* "This experiment strikes me as a clever and reliable invention; but tell us what you concluded from the result." *Salviati answers:* ".... I have not been able to ascertain with certainty whether the appearance of the opposite light was instantaneous or not; but if not instantaneous, it is extraordinarily rapid." In this example one finds everything that is desirable in a physicist: imagination in inventing experiments, skill, objective reporting of results, correct estimate of experimental errors.

Besides physics, there is another aspect of Galilean philosophy which goes beyond the limits of any branch of science and which, if we so wished, we could call to mind every day of our lives. But this aspect has often been confused with the problem of the character of Galileo and has been for three centuries the subject of a debate going far beyond the controversy on his philosophical approach. This debate is centered on the value of scientific culture in terms of moral and religious principles. In this respect, it is worth remarking that a drama (intentionally written with all the artistic imagination required to synthesize the greatness and the misery of our scientific and technical society) succeeded in stirring a new polemic about the deeper human roots of that very debate.

It is my opinion that, when looking at these roots, it is of very limited interest to know whether or not Galileo bought his first telescope from a Dutch merchant. But it seems to me essential to know that, having a telescope in his hands, after weeks of observations repeated over and over again to check the power and reliability of the instrument in magnifying terrestrial objects far away, he raised it toward the sky with absolute faith in the keenness of his senses mediated and enhanced by an instrument contrived by man. The point that seems essential to me is that he proved through his eager pursuit of knowledge and the unprejudiced use of his intellect — by discovering mountains on the moon, spots on the sun, the satellites of Jupiter, and many new stars never seen before — that he had more faith in his instruments than in the mystical perfection of the sky.

Before Galileo, instruments and machines were used only to increase the efficiency of human and animal labor, while after him, machines and instruments became the means to hew down the fence that kept within extremely narrow limits man's perception of the world.

Today, thanks to optical or radar telescopes, we "see" things that are extremely far away from us: electronic devices and instruments allow us to "see" a virus or to follow the track of an electron; we "hear" sound signals emitted by a bee or a bat; we measure time with electronic or atomic clocks; we know when and where a single photon has been absorbed.

At this point, one may argue that this "technical" development was more or less on the way and that in this sense Galileo was only the most eminent man of his time. This is certainly true; however, there is one thing which distinguishes him from all the others and which is unrelated to any scientific achievement. The *Sidereus Nuncius* — the booklet of thirty-five pages in which his main astronomical discoveries are condensed — is practically his last work written in Latin, the language of the scholars of his time. Thereafter, he intentionally wrote in the vulgar tongue so as to include in his audience not only scholars but all people able to think for themselves.

This is the last point I would like to consider. The *Sidereus Nuncius* was published on March 12, 1610. In September, he moved from Padua to Florence and became "Matematico primario dello Studio di Pisa e filosofo del Serenissimo Granduca senza obbligo di leggere e di risiedere nè nello Studio nè nella citta di Pisa etc., . . ." which means, in addition to a salary comparable with the salary of an American Nobel Prize winner and the elegant title, that he had no obligations whatever with respect to teaching and residence.

But the *Sidereus Nuncius*, in less than one year, stirred a violent and large debate which involved the highest authorities of the Catholic Church and of science, such as Cardinal Bellarmino and Kepler, as well as thousands of laymen. Considering the content of this booklet, this appears today rather predictable. However, Galileo was shocked, and from that time — from 1611 to July 6, 1633, the day on which he left Rome, the theater of his ignominy — he conceived a vast and ambitious program: a project to diffuse over all intelligent men the great assets of the new scientific culture.

Free from all duties, finally well settled economically, instead of writing the long-conceived book on mechanics, instead of extending his explorations of the sky, he started what we may call a political campaign in defense of a new society potentially free from prejudice and oriented toward irreversible progress.

This statement is not arbitrary or overdone, and well-qualified historians agree with it. We may refer here to the many letters written by him; for instance, that to Benedetto Castelli (1613) and that to the Principessa Cristina di Lorena (1615) where, with his basically catholic spirit, he tries to demonstrate the possible coexistence (not the consistency) of Catholic dogma and Copernican doctrine. But to demonstrate the statement, it suffices to read the *Dialogue Concerning the Two Great World Systems*, appreciating its general frame and presentation as an open debate. According to his words, "the true philosophers, the lovers of the true, should not be irritated, but knowing to have erroneously thought would thank who showed to them the very true." Listen to his language, the language of the people, written in a splendid style, but elucidating the essentials of the problems. With this language, conscious of the significance and value of what he and the scholars of the sixteenth century had discovered, he wanted to raise from ignorance and prejudice the generations to come. In this respect, the battle to defend the Copernican system goes far beyond the struggle for an idea thought to be right. It is the expression of a faith, the faith that a free human being has the right and the power to fight perennially against fictitious dogma, intellectual and moral idleness. This seems to me the greatest legacy of Galileo. In this sense, he is also the first man of the "enlightenment."

As stated clearly quite a few times in the penetrating and very gratifying discussions of these two days, certainly in scientific revolution he is at one of the highest peaks, though not alone. However, precursor and prophet at the same time, he is the Socrates of this revolution and the only one. This statement is not a personal fantasy. The new religious trends have condemned Copernicus and those who supported his ideas. To consider some significant examples, Kepler and Descartes, in private letters written to friends, strongly criticized Galileo's attitude, stating that his behavior was bold and imprudent.

I would thus conclude that in modern times, from the Renaissance on, there has been no philosopher nor philosophy which has exerted a deeper influence on history than the influence exerted by the works and troubled life of Galileo In many ways, although for widely varying reasons, we may be tempted to compare him to Aristotle.

Aristotle's thought and, even more, his ideals of perfection, found in Thomas Aquinas and in Christianity the robust walls that defended, for over a thousand years, their integrity and immense prestige. Galileo's thought found in the essential rationality and simplicity which pertain to science the power to hand itself down, from one generation to the next, in an irreversible progress that knows no setbacks. However, one has to admit that Galileo is not the Aristotle of modern times: his presence is not at all equivalent to the lasting influence of Thomas' doctrine in defending moral and intellectual principles during the Middle Ages.

Galileo's influence was determinant in the eighteenth century. This was the century of the triumph of human reason; the century in which the discovery of Newton's laws was a source of light along the intellectual and moral road of the future, not limited to the circle of scholars, but also including many of the alert bourgeois, profoundly affected by their reading of the encyclopedia. It was the century in which science was a determining force in provoking the most enlightened social revolutions, the American and the French. But since the first decades of the nineteenth century, a great divorce has occurred between science and technique. The new trend, which has changed many essential features of human society, was technical development. With the industrial revolution, the feedback reaction between science and technique, between discovery and invention, becomes more and more rapid; but, at the same time, the scientist increasingly returns to the position of the scholar intellectually bound only to other scholars. The scientific value of the discoveries of Volta, Ampère, Faraday, Fresnel, Gibbs, Maxwell, and Hertz reached the crowd of *honnêtes hommes* through the inventions of Watt, a watchmaker, and Pacinotti and Gramme, one a rather modest physicist, the other a brilliant, aggressive engineer, etc., . . ., up to Marconi, a very ingenious fellow, whose intellectual limitations were comparable with his moral ones.

Nowadays, with respect to the nineteenth century, the only noticeable difference is that the scale of time is extremely contracted. The feedback between pure and applied science is so rapid that the feeling of scientific evolution penetrates daily into most men, innocently, but brutally, through the offer of an increasingly leisured life.

At the same time, the comprehension of the more general value of science is more and more confused. One meets daily strangely biased and distorted ideas even in gifted persons whose approach to scientific culture goes from lasting memories of the horrors of the last war to a superficial, almost ridiculous, exaltation of technical development as the highest mark of the human mind. This seems to me the reason why we have lost the greatest message of Galileo. In the years which followed the 22nd of June 1633, the day of abjuration, Galileo returned to pure science. Only four years later, the *Dialogues Concerning Two New Sciences* was published in Holland. But the return to pure science was not an abjuration of his faith in the general moral and intellectual value of science. This last work of Galileo is actually his greatest contribution to modern civilization. Here he no longer speaks polemically for or against the Copernican system; he speaks calmly and serenely of the first discoveries in physics; he uses this means to convey to all men the high dignity of rationality and freedom. How many modern scientists and new scholars contribute consciously to the increase of this human dignity?

At the beginning of my presentation I said that my interpretation of Galileo's influence on modern society would suffer from great professional and personal distortion. After all, I am a physicist and a Florentine. If I had to answer this last question, this distortion would be far greater. I leave it to you to answer.

3

NORWOOD RUSSELL HANSON

GALILEO'S REAL DISCOVERIES
IN DYNAMICS

Giants are frightening at close range. One views them with detachment only from far off. A giant within history of science is no different. To give hindsight full play, we *need* to be 400 years distant from an Olympian. How else can mere mortals take the measure of Galileo's mixture of imagination, intellect, and courage?[1] His contemporaries idolatrized him, or tugged back at his sandals — depending on whether they were frightened or inspired. At our remove fright is no longer likely. But even inspiration must be restrained for complete objectivity. Centuries of scholarship to the contrary notwithstanding, Galileo was not a great experimental scientist. He was no experimental scientist at all; not as we would know one. Nor was he a powerful theoretical thinker, surely not within technical mechanics. But he left a mathematical stamp on nature, the full imprint of which is still felt by physicists and natural philosophers.

[1]Galileo Galilei, born in Pisa, February 1564 — the year when Michelangelo, Vesalius, and Calvin died, and the year when Shakespeare was born.

Let me urge these theses *seriatim;* first, that Galileo was no experimentalist.

I

My first exposure to Galileo was to "the Father of Experimental Science." Apparently he was the first fully to appreciate precise laboratory measurement, careful experimental controls, and the repetition of all determinations of significant parameters. He was the earliest who, apparently, let the natural world write *its own* description. He did not force scholastic preconceptions on matter; rather, mathematical physics was for him nature's autobiography. Galileo's laws, such as that $s=\frac{1}{2}at^2$, were *generalizations* (I was told) from stacks of repeated measurements, trials, observations, and tests; ever finer adjustments, ever more precision and calibration, ever more heaping up of the raw facts. One counterinstance made him cheerfully abandon any thus-discredited law claim, so strict were his empirical sensibilities. Not until Galileo, continues the myth, was physics perceived to be the factual and essentially observational discipline it really is.[2]

Purely myth all this surely is. It is a fantasy of facts about Galileo, and a fantasy about past and present physics — dreamed up by commentators who (perhaps) understand too little of both. What to say of one, like Galileo, for whom experiments were only *demonstrations* of what reason and reflection and argument have already revealed? *Just* that he was not really an empiricist at all? No. Such a man may tell the truths of physics better than "dust-bowl experimentalists." Perhaps being an empiricist in the full sense is being more than a fact-grubbing pebble-counter. Galileo was

[2]Thus e.g., "Galileo always begins with experiential premises." Seeger, R. J., in *American Journal of Physics*, March 1964.

never prostrate before nature's mere minutiae. He was never seduced by the attractions of precision for its own sake or by the Sangreal of finer, ever finer, tests and measurements. Yet he unraveled some critical factual knots within the history of thought.

For him laws of nature were not just superdescriptions generated *out* of observations. Rather, observations were themselves intelligible only insofar as they were informed by laws.[3] Laws constituted the *rationale* of nature; Galileo's acute demonstrations were just lively demonstrations of that rationale. To comprehend the structural plan of the physical world required not busy elbows, dextrous fingers, and sharp eyes. It required hard thinking about the nature of Nature — about the *essential* form and format of physical processes and phenomena.[4]

This is not to suggest that Galileo, like a romantic idealist, snubbed the facts of sense evidence. Hardly.[5] He was ever ready to consider new ideas and unorthodox techniques with which to acquire knowledge. Uncannily, he always hit on observations (often commonplace ones), which probed and provoked immense theoretical issues; he *could* have seen the universe in a grain of sand! That water rises only to 32 feet in suction pumps was a lens for his philosophical vision. But again, it was physical theory which

[3]"It seemed that the Laws of Motion *could not be false*, that is, it was inconceivable that any alternative propositions could be valid." Hall, A. R. *From Galileo to Newton* (Harper, 1963), p. 38.

[4]"Apriori geometrical reasoning seemed to make experiment superfluous." Hall, *op. cit.*, p. 55.

[5]". . . one may learn with all the certainty of sense evidence that the moon is not robed in a smooth and polished surface. . . ." Galileo, *The Sidereal Messenger*. Cf. also: ". . . if his [Aristotle's] knowledge had included our present sensory evidence — he too would have granted our conclusions." *Letters on Sunspots*.

was beheld by such vision, not the making of further experimental lenses for inquiry *per se*. Granted, Galileo is renowned for his perfection of instruments; the proportional compass (1596), the thermoscope (1602), and, most significantly, the telescope (1609) were perception-aids with which he observed what men had never encountered before.[6] But this remarkable creativity should be charged to technical development, to curiosity, and to the deepest respect for nature *as it is*. Nowhere does Galileo gravely pronounce Baconian principles, rigorous adherence to which might torture truths out of natural subject matters. The idea of *inertia*, although imperfectly formulated by Galileo, was a great conceptual and theoretical achievement.[7] But so far as leaving it to experiment and observation to corroborate that concept, Galileo could never have understood such a suggestion. Factual details (like rococo tracery) confuse the intellect and cloud the imagination; only these latter faculties can apprehend and comprehend the structure of nature beneath the deceptive superficialities which constitute the surface of things.[8]

[6]In 1586 he wrote his first scientific paper, *La Bilancetta (The Little Balance)*, concerning a hydrostatic balance for directly reading analyses of gold-silver mixtures. He made 100 telescopes, the most powerful achieving a magnification of 33 times. He optically resolved the Milky Way into component stars. He saw Jupiter's moons, the mountains on our moon, and the phases of Venus — all for the first time by man.

[7]Galileo clung to the Aristotelian distinction between naturally occurring motions (uniform and circular) and forced ones (accelerated and rectilinear).

[8]"Credit is also due Galileo for his discoveries with the telescope. Nevertheless, all that was really required here was primarily sight. . . ." Seeger, *op. cit.* How ironic, also, that just before being struck blind, Galileo's final discovery (1637) was of the moon's librations. But, even without vision, he remained a Natural Philosopher *non pareil*.

II

Galileo's reflections take one to the edge of imagination. Continually we are swept to the consideration of *limits* of rectilinear motion, as traced through media of diminishing density — ultimately complete *vacua*. The processes he discusses may be *nonterminating;* they may, indeed, require an *infinite* amount of time. This man stretched his readers' minds to the utmost: in thought he dilutes to the vanishing point the accidental colors of objects. He sharpens and straightens their dimensions and edges (razorlike). He is ever subtly smoothing their motions—leaving us at last with the ideally abstract case: colorless, tasteless, soundless, frictionless. This abstraction lacks the thousand accidental features that actual phenomena are heir to. Thus does Galileo force us to mark and remark the essential formal aspects of dynamical phenomena. Thus does physics seem increasingly like pure mathematics, *plus* some additional parameters involving masses, forces, velocities, etc. Indeed, whatever in nature could not be so managed seemed to Galileo not amenable to proper physical analysis at all. Mere descriptions of accidental, local phenomena suffice for natural history — "bug hunting" — but not for natural philosophy.

Hence laws of nature could not possibly be descriptive generalizations for Galileo, however precisely generated and carefully culled. Rather, laws set out the conceptual "framework features" of dynamical phenomena. These must be comprehended before their factual embodiments (objects and events) can ever be perceived intelligibly.[9]   Thus

[9]He who lacks all understanding of why $2 + 2$ equals 4, can hardly be on guard against contingencies such as a couple of apples being added to a couple of pears and thereby generating *five* pieces of fruit! To know what's wrong here does not require a polling of fruiterers: it requires knowing in advance that $2 + 2 = 4$.

the laws must somehow precede our confrontations with phenomena — psychologically, logically, and conceptually. Else there could be nothing lawlike in *our* experience of phenomena. Laws considered as a composite residue from multiple exposures to "mere" phenoma — such a notion would have decomposed Galileo's credulity. Rightly so. There are no objects, processes, or facts *simpliciter*; an object *x* is never *just* seen, never *just* experienced in phenomenological isolation, nor *just* known in an epistemological vacuum. It is seen *as* something or other; it is experienced as this or that *kind* of thing; it is known to have these *properties* rather than those. Processes are observed to have *this* direction or *that*, this development and fulfillment or that particular disintegration.[10] Facts are always facts *about* or *with respect to* or set out *in terms of* some theoretical framework. Should the framework deliquesce, the objects, processes, and facts will dissolve conceptually.[11] Where now are the "facts" of alchemy, of phlogiston theory? Or must we grant that no observations ever really supported such frameworks of ideas? Where can one now locate a sample of caloric, or a magnetic effluvium? How easy and doctrinaire to remark these as chimera, as illusions of fact. They are actually once-descriptive references whose supporting rationale has disappeared. Their articulators were, in their way, dedicated empiricists, groping, struggling, to delineate *the facts* concerning intricacies of a near-incomprehensible world. But effluvia, caloric, phlogiston,

[10]Hanson, N. R., *Patterns of Discovery*, Cambridge University Press, 1958.

[11]"If we in our thoughts attempt to divest matter of its powers of resisting and moving, it ceases to be matter, according to our conceptions and we can no longer reason upon it with any distinctness...." Whewell, W., *Astronomy and General Physics* (London, 1834), pp. 211, 212.

influences — virtues, humors, and essences — harmonies, attractions, and powers — these are no longer sustained by laws, as once they appeared to be — and as *our* now-recorded facts, processes, and objects seem so surely to be. But the negative-energy electron, the luminiferous ether, and the planet Vulcan are not so long parted from the scientific stage. May not the solid acquisitions of our own laboratory performances yet grow pale before the chilling winds of new doctrine — doctrine opposed to our presently accepted theories?

Physics is an open-ended investigation of nature. Yesterday's data, recast within tomorrow's theories, may depict yet a different world even to the closest observers. J. J. Thomson could see everything that Compton saw, but not in the same way. [12] Kepler espied nothing which Tycho Brahe lacked the capacity to observe — but their observations cohered very differently.[13]

And, save for his telescopic work, little within Galileo's perceptual field had not been perceived (element for element) by earlier natural philosophers.[14] Yet he perceived what they could not: he discovered connections and relations between known elements of inquiry — he found their organization. Galileo's theoretical vision made him a *better* empiricist than his contemporaries;[15] better even than our

[12]Cf. in *The Philosophical Magazine*, articles between 1926-1928.

[13]Kepler, *De Motibus Stellae Martis*, in Astronomia Nova (München, 1937-).

[14]E.g., Joannes Philoponus noted in 533 A.D. that two objects of vastly different weights would nonetheless fall with little difference in the times. Simon Stevin and Johan de Groot had done the experiment in 1586.

[15]"Rarely did Galileo claim that the Aristotelians erred in their facts because they had not experimented. . . ." Hall, *op. cit.*, p. 75.

statistics-bound, data-mongering contemporaries. It enabled him to see *more* of the world than they could, or can. He pierced the surface of dynamical events, conceiving within them a mathematical order analogous to what Euclid had perceived in the space all round him. Euclid geometrized space. Thereby he made its observed properties intelligible. Galileo mathematicized dynamics, and thereby he made its *facts* an object of philosophical study.[16]

What, then, was *discovery* to Galileo? It was the perception of cohesive, mathematical structure within the buzzing detail of experience. For him, every falling coin, every windblown leaf, every new moon was a special kind of anomaly, an occasion for inquiry. Phenomena like these, familiar, but not understood, were the windows through which the anatomy of the universe could be witnessed, if one but focused the appropriate mathematical lens. Through lenses of his own design Galileo had seen the moon as terrestrial. So also he viewed dynamical events through algebraic lenses ground by his own intellect. To have perceived that *all* of nature was visible through such lenses — more, to have urged that its capacity to *be* so viewed was the defining characteristic of what we are entitled to call "nature" — *there* is the synoptic discovery of this visionary student of the facts. All his other findings are subordinate to, and supportive of, this one brilliant insight. For now the world lay before Galileo, as before Adam, virtually undiscovered, in facts-as-yet-unseen. Here was the first modern natural philosopher with the eyes of a mathematical physicist. Hence, for him, as with the ancient Archimedes (and as with

[16]Of course, the *Dialogues* (1632) is a geometry of circles. The *Discourses* (1638) concern rectilinear motion primarily inasmuch as Galileo there confines himself to the small-scale. Cf. Hall, *op. cit.,* p. 52.

Newton later), to look anywhere — to see and to understand the phenomena before one — was to *discover*. Galileo had found the code of physical existence — the rest was largely decipherment. The code soon came to be recognized as being infinitely more complex than Galileo imagined. But the fundamental insight is not different, as the personages of Lagrange, Laplace, and Leverrier, of Clerk Maxwell and Willard Gibbs, of Dirac, Heisenberg, Pauli, Schrödinger, and von Neumann, and many other modern heroes, all make abundantly clear. These are the names of empiricists possessed of the compound vision of mathematicians. They too tell the truth about the facts of nature; only, as with Galileo, they can see those facts more fully than searchers with mathematically untrained eyes.

Consider all this as it bears on but one tiny portion of Galileo's work.[17]

Galileo had argued that a sphere rolling down a plane on one side of a room would roll across the floor and up a plane on the opposite side. Ignoring friction, the sphere will ascend the second plane to just that height (above the floor) from which it had been released on the first plane. What the sphere acquires in its descent is thus equal to driving it back up to its original height on the second slope.

Incline the second plane less and less steeply to the floor. The sphere will still "seek" a height on that plane equal to that from which it started. As the ascent line gets closer to the floor, the sphere travels farther along that plane "in order to" resume its original height. As the angle between the floor and the second plane gets closer to zero, the distance the sphere will travel along it will increase; it will,

---

[17]Primarily from the *Discourses* although the following is anticipated in the *Dialogues*.

indeed, proceed toward an *infinite* length of travel as the angle inclination proceeds toward the limit *zero*.

Thus a sphere moving on an *ideal* (frictionless) floor will proceed along a straight line to infinity. Only something like our second inclined plane (or like friction, or air resistance) prevents this by taking from the sphere just what distinguished it from a sphere at rest.

Galileo's reflections[18] could have gone a little further. This much is convincing as to the nonterminating, rectilinear character of force-free motion. But that such motion will be *uniform* Galileo assumed to follow qualitatively from his "thought experiment"; either that, or it seems to follow from his idea of "force-free motion."[19] But why assume what is

[18]*Discourses Concerning the Two New Sciences* (trans. Crew and de Salvio), Northwestern University, 1939 — IIIrd Day, pp. 242–248.

[19]As whenever the First Law is characterized as being but a limiting case of the Second Law, i.e., when $\Sigma F = 0$ it follows that $a = 0$ (whether $m = 0$ or > 0). That is, $d^2x/dt^2 = 0$; $d^2y/dt^2 = 0$; $d^2z/dt^2 = 0$: the second time derivatives of coordinates x, y, z vanish when a body is force-free. From this much, however, one can infer the rectilinearity of an inertial path only by building that concept *into* "force-free."

. . . .

But along a horizontal plane the motion is uniform since here it experiences neither acceleration nor retardation: . . .

. . . .

Furthermore we may remark that any velocity once imparted to a moving body will be rigidly maintained as long as the external causes of acceleration or retardation are removed, a condition which is found only on horizontal planes; for in the case of planes which slope downwards there is already present a cause of acceleration, while on planes sloping upward there is retardation; from this it follows that motion along a horizontal plane is perpetual; for, if the velocity be uniform, it cannot be diminished or slackened much less destroyed. Further, although any velocity which a body may have acquired through natural fall is permanently maintained so far as its own nature (*suapte natura*) is concerned, yet it must be

demonstrable? Think of all those inclined planes which could nest within the angle between our secondary plane and the floor. As the plane is lowered, every intervening angle will have been traversed by the plane and by the ascending sphere. Imagine a line parallel with the floor (but lower than the original height from which the sphere descended). A line could then be drawn through all those possible inclinations to which we just referred. Consider the intersection of that line with each of these inclined planes. At each such intersection note the deceleration of the ascending sphere (the rate at which its velocity is falling off as it climbs the secondary plane). We expect the deceleration to be greater on a steeply inclined plane than it would be at the corresponding point on a plane of shallow inclination. As this plane is "flattened" down to where it coincides with the floor, the value of the deceleration variable (as it "moves" along the line) will itself decrease. When the plane does join the floor, the deceleration will be zero.[20] A similar argument

remembered that if, after descent along a plane inclined downwards the body is deflected to a plane inclined upwards, there is already existing in this latter plane a cause of retardation; for in any such plane this same body is subject to a natural acceleration downwards. Accordingly there we have the supposition of two different states, namely, the velocity acquired during the preceding which if acting alone would carry the body at a uniform rate to infinity, and the velocity which results from a natural acceleration downwards common to all bodies. It seems altogether reasonable, therefore, if we wish to trace the future history of a body which has descended along some inclined plane and has been deflected along some plane inclined upwards, for us to assume that the maximum speed acquired during descent is permanently maintained during the ascent. In the ascent, however, there supervenes a natural inclination downwards, namely, a notion which, starting from rest, is accelerated at the usual rate.

Galileo, *op. cit.*, pp. 215–16.

[20]For now the plane and the line "intersect" only at infinity.

applies for acceleration. But the point is that the uniformity of a body's (force-free) motion can be argued for: it need not be assumed.[21]

The ideas of "rectilinearity," "motion *ad infinitum*," "uniform," and "force-free" are interdependent conceptions within Galileo's mechanics. One can treat uniform, rectilinear motion *ad infinitum* as itself built into the notion "force-free" (as part of the latter's semantical content). Thinking of a body free of impressed forces would then just be to think of a body either at rest, or in uniform, rectilinear motion. But this game can also be played by packing "force-free" into one of the other concepts — uniform, or rectilinear, or motion *ad infinitum*. And so on.

Thus one thing learned in trying to understand Galileo's "Law of Terrestrial Inertia" is that its terms are semantically linked. The meaning of each of its terms "unpacks" sometimes from the others; but sometimes the meaning of these others unpacks from the first. Which are "the contained," and which the semantical "containers," affects the exposition of any mechanical theory built thereupon. In this way one can distinguish the mechanical theories of Galileo, of Lagrange, and of Hertz. Archimedes longed for an immovable platform away from which to lever the world; so also every physical theory requires a set of stable, primitive conceptions in terms of which all its other terms can be explicated. Although Galileo, Lagrange, and Hertz gave their energies to the same theory, classical mechanics, they chose different semantical platforms on which to fix their fundamental laws; hence they confronted their further theoretical problems in different conceptual postures.

The Law of Inertia is thus really a family of schemata,

[21]Compare Mach, *op. cit.*, pp. 168–169. And see again the first line in the quotation from Galileo in ftn. 19.

and this is so even in Galileo's formulation. The essentially algorithmic function of the law is contained in this fact: the theoretician can trace whatever genealogy of concepts he chooses from little more than his first decision to invest Galileo's law with *this* semantical structure rather than *that*.

I have considered a typical Galilean statement of the law. We have noted also the reflections which made it seem plausible to Galileo and his successors as well as the semantical decisions which will, in different formalizations of the theory, generate different meaning-relations among the constituent terms within the law: sometimes A, B, and C will be semantically primitive and D will be derived, sometimes D will be primitive. One function of Galileo's law consists in such interrelating of mechanical concepts. Hence, a Mach and a Hertz may interrelate these terms differently; the law does different work within their theories — different even from what it did within Galileo's reflections.

III

I have also characterized as mythical the oft-heard claim that Galileo was a great experimentalist. His ingenuity with instruments must not be confused with the repetitive data-gathering typical of genuine empirical science. Indirectly, all this is clear from his attitude toward laws of nature; for Galileo these are never summaries of observed phenomena. Rather they are the "pure cases" through which the observations become intelligible: this, even though some "nonobservables" may figure in the law-statements themselves.

These nonobservables, in Galileo's "Laws of Dynamics," concern the numerical *limits* of sequences (considered in spatial and/or temporal contexts), the physical *limits* of processes (such things as pure vacua and instantaneous velocities); references to infinities and infinitudes, "sharp" instants and geometrical points, planes without edges, space of indefinitely great dimensions — these references abound in *The Dialogues* and in *The Discourses*. These make nature tractable and mathematical, without the insignificant local "accidents" of faded colors, uneven textures, odors, impurities, crude calibration, and lopsided carpentry. Understanding thus the structure of dynamical phenomena drew Galileo to perceive the formal framework within which such events occurred — to comprehend these events fully required "Euclidean" treatment, founded on abstract, "pure," nonfactual, and wholly general "limit-ideas." Thus, just as *"ad infinitum"* dominates Euclid's Fifth Axiom, so also *ad infinitum* figures essentially in Galileo's Law of Terrestrial Inertia. He imparted a geometrical *dénouement* to the simplest demonstration — the famous (or infamous) inclined-plane "experiment." At one "end" this revealed the "Law of Freely Falling Bodies" (when the plane was tipped up vertically), and at the other "end" the Law of Terrestrial Inertia (when the plane was lowered level with the earth's surface).[22] Let us consider this last again, in even more detail. We have seen what it meant as a discovery for Galileo. What did it mean in the discoveries of his successors? What *must* it have come to mean? After all, expressions like "rectilinearity," "motion *ad infinitum*," "uniform," "force-free," "frictionless," etc. — although obvious to one who sees nature through a geometer's eyes — must yet be "cashed" in the actual observations of *this* world. An expression lacking operational interpretation is indistinguishable from jabberwocky, at least in the hallowed halls of the history of physics.

Galileo's Law of Terrestrial Inertia is not a linguistic

[22]And by suitable combinations of both references one generates the "Laws of Parabolic Trajectories" in ballistics.

translating-device. It is not concerned only with the sub-stitutability of terms inside a mechanical game. It began in factual opposition to an alternative claim, itself quite amenable to observational tests. The Ancients' contention that continued application of force was necessary for motion to continue, meant simply that without it motion would cease.[23] All terrestrial bodies would therefore come to rest (sooner or later) were no further motive power applied. As a description of what we observe as engineers, physicists, and travelers, the Ancients' claim seems not only substanti-*able*, but substantiat*ed in fact*. Its negation ought also to be vulnerable to factual inquiry; indeed since we take that negation as a physical basis for much of the last four hun-dred years in science, Galileo's Law of Inertia should also be substantiat*ed in fact*, at least as directly and plausibly as the ancient "law." It was that observational plausibility which made the older view basic to Aristotle's scientific work. Despite so many initial observations to the contrary, Gali-leo's Law of Terrestrial Inertia should also be referable to demonstrable facts, which (however nonobvious) will none-theless anchor our science of mechanics in an observational foundation of physical truth. In *The Discourses*, as we saw earlier, Galileo begins the demonstration.

If, however, we restate the law in its most transparent form, it will read as follows:

IF THERE WERE A PARTICLE FREE OF UNBALANCED, EXTERNAL FORCES, *THEN* IT WOULD EITHER RE-MAIN ABSOLUTELY AT REST, OR WOULD MANIFEST UNIFORM RECTILINEAR MOTION *AD INFINITUM*.

Here the meaning-content of the law is clearer than any-where in *The Discourses*. It is what logicians call "an un-

[23]By the principle: "*cessante causa cessat et effectus*."

fulfilled hypothetical" or "a counterfactual conditional."
We have no reason for supposing that particles free of unbalanced external forces do exist. But the law tells us what
would obtain with such particles *if* they did. This has the
doubly awkward consequence that (1) we (like Galileo) cannot investigate the properties of such bodies, and (2) the
law, being hypothetical, cannot be shown to be false. It
cannot even be shown to be *falsifiable*, something which
many take as a necessary condition for meaningfulness
within science. An unfalsifiable claim — one which is com-
patible with anything — is termed "insignificant." Thus
that the universe shrank last night, being now one billionth
part smaller than yesterday (including ourselves, measuring
instruments, theodolites, micrometers, diffraction gratings,
the wavelengths of standard radiation, elementary particles,
etc.), this claim, since *ex hypothesi* it cannot be falsified, is
physically meaningless. Does the counterfactuality of the
Law of Inertia put it into this same class? Not quite. When
linked with a network of other physical assumptions, the
law does have testable consequences.[24] This is not true of
the "shrunken universe" claim: given any two moving
bodies, one demonstrably freer of external forces than the
other, that one body will approximate (more closely than the
other) to uniform, rectilinear motion *ad infinitum* — although it can never push to the formal limit of perfect inertial motion. Semantical difficulties arise, however, in this
idea of pushing an approximation "to its formal limit"; how
can one body move "closer to" infinity than another? The
remark is unintelligible as it stands. But now another per-
plexing difficulty obtrudes.

[24]Only by imagining an impossible situation can a clear and simple
law of fall be formulated, and only by possessing that law is it possible
to comprehend the complex things that actually happen.
Hall, *op. cit.*, p. 63.

Reflect on this: not only has no one ever encountered a force-free body — but also, the expressions "uniform" and "rectilinear," to have operational significance and physical meaning, must be coordinated with measuring techniques. How do we establish a motion as rectilinear and uniform? We set up coordinates by reference to which a point's translation from x, y, z at t (to x', y', z' at $t + \Delta t$) may correspond to a rectilinear and uniform Cartesian translation within the spaces defined. This is not an exercise in geometry; it is no exploration of some abstract space. Quite the contrary. It requires setting up physical coordinates, determined by actual objects; when these are assumed as fixed, they allow the relational, intrageometrical distinctions necessary for describing the point's trace [within] the resulting reference frame.

Suppose the universe consisted in one and only one punctiform mass. Of its mechanical behavior nothing could be said.[25] To claim of that mass that it moves uniformly along a rectilinear path, it is necessary to fix physical coordinates by assuming *other* masses to be anchored.[26] How many others? One at the zero point and three others out along the coordinates! Without these as absolutely immobile the motion of our original particle could not be described as uniform and rectilinear; it could not be said to be in motion at all! This would require at least five particles. Any particle one describes as moving uniformly and rectilinearly must be but one particle in a universe containing

[25]This very supposition is internally inconsistent for anyone who accepts Mach's kinetic definition of *mass*. Since *ex hypothesi* a single particle cannot interact with other particles, it is idle to discuss its mass in Machian terms. Are there other meaningful terms?

[26]This already wrecks the supposition.

five — the specimen-particle and the four coordinate-fixers. But no particle within such a universe can be free of external, unbalanced forces — a simple inference from the "Law of Universal Gravitation."[27]

So the counterfactual character of Galileo's law stands not merely as an observation that no bodies *are* found to be force-free, but rather as a consequence of there being no body whose motion is uniform and rectilinear which could possibly be force-free. Any alternative crushes the gravitational cornerstone of mechanics. Appraisals of the law's logical status are pierced by this point. The law thus refers to entities not such that, although never observed, they remain observ*able*. Rather, they are unobservable in physical principle. This is a conceptual truth, not a factual one. Either the law conflicts with our conception of physical meaning, or it conflicts with other laws of mechanics. Either way, it is difficult to understand.

Concerning the number of particles needed to fix coordinates, it might be argued that 4 is too many. With a zero-point particle and two coordinates determined by 2 further bodies, a third dimension is easily "mapped away" from the plane so defined. But this eradicates also the remaining 3 particles; thus we can always determine from the zero point 2 perpendiculars normal to each other. But then only one of these last 2 need remain; the first coordinate line can be laid out in any arbitrary direction from the zero-point particle, it being easy to construct "imaginary" perpendiculars on that. *But there the reduction halts.* For the zero point must, as a matter of physical intelligibility, be construed as a fixed particle, out from which a reference frame

---

[27]"Any two particles in the universe are such that they attract each other directly as their masses, and inversely as the square of the distance between them."

may be constructed.[28] Our earlier arguments remain un-affected, therefore. In order to say of any particle that its motion is uniform and rectilinear, it must be one member of at least a 2-particle universe. It remains logically impossible, then, both for that particle to be force-free and for the rest of mechanics to be true.[29]

Either dynamical theory is false, or it is meaningless to suppose Galileo's law could be other than hypothetical and counterfactual-in-principle! The function of the law, within physical theory, is thus difficult to assess. Is it "true" although counterfactual? What does it do?

The rectilinearity part of Galileo's law is thus an operational puzzle.

Operationally to ensure that the motion is *uniform*, one needs a measuring rod in our barren 2-particle universe. A metric must be fixed within the reference frame construct-

---

[28]This zero-point particle is identical to Neumann's "body alpha."

[29]"If every place is relative then every motion is relative and as motion cannot be understood without a determination of its direction which in its turn cannot be understood except in relation to our or some other body. Up, down, right, left, all directions and places are based on some relation and it is necessary to suppose another body distinct from the moving one . . . so that motion is given in relation to which it exists, or generally there cannot be any relation, if there are no terms to be related.

"Therefore if we suppose that everything is annihilated except one globe, it would be impossible to imagine any movements of that globe.

"Let us imagine two globes and that besides them nothing else material exists, then the motion in a circle of these two globes round their common centre cannot be imagined. But suppose that the heaven of fixed stars was suddenly created and we shall be in a position to imagine the motion of the globes by their relative position to the different parts of heaven."

From Berkeley, *De Motu* (written thirty years after the publication of the *Principia* of Newton).

ible upon the zero-particle. For how can we establish a motion as uniform other than by determining that it traverses equal spaces in equal times (?), which is just what "uniform motion" means.[30] The obvious way of ensuring that the spaces are equal is to lay a measuring rod first against one translation-segment and then against another. If the ends of the segments coincide with the ends of the rod, then the spaces are equal. But saying this assumes that the rod suffers no deformation from one trajectory-segment to another. The assumption cannot rest on other reasoning inside classical mechanics — within matter theory, kinetic theory, and elasticity theory; this would be circular. These are derivative subsections within classical mechanics, which itself depends on the *meaning* of Galileo's law. So that law cannot be substantiated by considerations which themselves rest on the assumption that the law is substantiated, an assumption built into all these derivative disciplines. No — that our measuring rod does not expand or contract during translation is itself fixed by convention. This suggests that even to understand the meaning of "uniform" in Galileo's Law of Inertia, a conventional appeal must be made to another cornerstone of mechanics, namely, that mere transportation does not alter the physical properties of a body. Of ordinary objects, we substantiate this within classical mechanics. But the ideal rod cannot be supported by such derivative disciplines, since the law is fundamental to classical mechanics as a whole, and hence to all its subdisciplines. The "uniformity" part of the law, therefore, requires for its understanding a sophisticated appeal to the conventionality

[30]Definition: By steady or uniform motion, I mean one in which the distances traversed by the moving particle during any equal intervals of time, are themselves equal.

Galileo, *Two New Sciences*, IIIrd Day, p. 191.

thesis. Such an exploration is necessary even to comprehend the meaning of the First Law of Motion.

These reflections have exciting consequences for the theoretical development of Galileo's law. Once it is apparent
that every physical reference frame is, and must be, itself
accelerated (i.e., is not free of impressed forces), it follows
that the concepts of *rectilinearity* and *infinity* must either
be defined physically in terms of such physical frames, or
else they, and the law, must assume an absolute space. If
rectilinearity and *infinity* are anchored to the properties and
behavior of actual objects, then these terms cannot be understood (as with Galileo) in their original geometric and num-
ber-theoretic manner. Their entire significance must depend
on the local peculiarities of particular physical spaces and
processes. Yet it was Galileo's objective that precision be
brought into studies of spaces and processes by translating
geometrical ideas from mathematics into physics. Were that
attitude to control fully our understanding of Galileo's Law
of Inertia, however, we would *have* to take pure geometrical
space, absolute space, as a force-free framework within
which all particles and processes reside. Without this one
cannot comprehend geometrically-founded statements
about the inertial motion of particles. Either the meaning
of *rectilinearity* and of *infinity* comes through to us (as it
did for Galileo) from pure geometry and number theory (in
which case absolute space is *the* envelope for all mechanical
subject matters) — or else these terms must be defined
through possible physical configurations (in which case the
law is in principle a counterfactual conditional, since it de-
notes entities which are nonobservable). Geometrical meaning or physical meaning: absolute space or counterfactual
conditionality. So our earlier discussion concerning Galileo's credentials as an empiricist has consequences. His

attitude towards natural philosophy was that of a geometer; it would have been the *geometrical* meaning for his Law of Inertia that would have drawn him towards the Newtonian concept of absolute space. Operationalist objections to this formulation might well have mattered to a genuine empiricist; it seems unlikely that they would have deterred Galileo in the slightest.[31]

I have suggested that every operational difficulty which attaches to local spaces whose geometrical coordinates are not fixed by particles — and this is how Galileo's presentation proceeds — is magnified when reference is made to absolute space itself! The complex later discussions by Leibniz, Euler, Laplace, Gauss, Hertz, and Mach, as well as Neumann's attempt to fuse pure geometry with "impure" physics by his postulated "body *alpha*" — all this lies implicitly in Galileo's *Discourses*. The insight of Galileo and of the giants of the Scientific Revolution was that the world, and its constituent processes, can be viewed as built on geometrical-mathematical lines.

Thus physics only "got off the ground" when it was mathematicized. Yet it often appears that mathematics continues *its* ascent only when its research is elevated on the unsolved problems of modern physics. Philosophical attitudes towards Galileo's Law of Inertia have oscillated accordingly. Either its meaning seems to be *imported* into physics from pure mathematics, or else that meaning is determined by physical consideration and then sent back to mathematicians for further formal development.

---

[31]"And when is it that we are supposed to test by experiment whether there is any difference to be discovered among these events of local motion . . . if the Earth remains forever in one or the other of these two states?"

Dialogues . . .

Let mathematics and physics be construed as but different aspects of one comprehensive discipline, a kind of mathematics-physics, the Galilean ideal. The Law of Inertia then comes into physics with predetermined geometrical meaning. It serves as a paradigm for all physics. But stop: now attend to the logical differences between mathematics and physics, differences clear enough to us but rather obscure to Galileo. Physical statements are true only in that their negations, although consistent, do not describe facts. The hunt must then be on for the *physical* meaning of "uniformity," "rectilinearity," and "infinity," not to mention terms like "equals," "is proportional to," "is commutative," "is of the second order in time," "is divergent,". . ., etc. Only by finding physical meanings for such expressions can one use them in making factually true physical statements. Mathematics and physics are logically different disciplines; the former can only occasionally solve the latter's problems via a kind of analogical transfer of formal operations to physical processes. Galileo's definition of physics in terms of mathematics is no longer fully acceptable.

Neumann's "body *alpha*" is a fascinating halfway house — something to which Galileo might have assented. Yearning for definitions of "uniformity," "rectilinearity," and "infinity" which would *not* be subject to overhaul within each new physical reference frame, Neumann "invented" *alpha*. Through this one body Neumann sought to fulfill Galileo's ideal, to convey the absolute definitions of Euclidean geometry into observational physics. One result would then have been that in a 2-particle universe one *could* recognize motion as rectilinear or otherwise, simply by reference to this physically fixed, but gravitationally inconsequential, body. However, physical unintelligibility is the upshot, both for *alpha* and for its relationship with the other particle.[32] What sense is there in describing *alpha* as "gravitationally inconsequental"? *Alpha* must then also be geometrically inconsequential for the purposes of physics. After Neumann, physicists have in unison pronounced, "Let no man join what nature hath sundered" — to wit, the formal creation of spaces and the physical description of bodies. Not even a giant like Galileo ever *really* joined these sundered disciplines.

IV

We have scrutinized Galileo's real discoveries in dynamics. They spilled from his primary "discovery" that nature could be viewed as from a draftsman's table, calculations on which captured the essence of phenomena. This primary discovery was not something "tripped over," as experimentalists sometimes trip over the unexpected. It was thought over. And it has been *fought* over ever since. For every Lagrange who, Galileo-like, sought to fuse physics with function theory, there has been a Mach nearby and "at the ready" to shoot withering stares at each mathematical-physical concept, insisting that they be "cashed" fully in operational terms — or else be banished thenceforth from the province of proper physics. Modern physicists discovered "the problem of physical meaning" when reflecting on Galileo's discovery that nature could be geometrized. Here too modern philosophy has made a discovery — a derivative discovery about meaning and semantics generally. For just as Galileo's pronouncements provoked Mach

---

[32]Compare Russell: "It seems evident that the question whether one body is at rest or in motion must have as good a meaning as the same question concerning any other body; and this seems sufficient to condemn Neumann's suggested escape from absolute motion." *The Principles of Mathematics*, 2nd edition, p. 464.

and Einstein and Bridgman to formulate what comes to us as "The Operational Criterion of Meaning," so also philosophers have looked more searchingly at the logical credentials of that criterion.

Should we demand that all concepts within physical theory be at once "negotiable" in terms of operations and observations — or else be manacled to mere metaphysics? The history of physics suggests this demand to be therapeutically valuable. Criticisms of the 'F' in Newton's "Law of Gravitation" and of the muddled ideas about gravitational "attraction" acting across immense empty distances — these led to a less anthropomorphic, a kinematical restatement of the law, this restatement being a partial condition for Einstein's "General Theory of Relativity." Similarily there was Newton's "Absolute Time and Space," within which *simultaneous* events (many light-years apart) might easily be thought of as occurring; Einstein again demanded the operational "cash value" of such a conception, and lo, we were made thereby to see how dependent on such operations as space-measurement and clock-synchronization our ideas of the universe really are. The moral? Any intratheoretical conception lacking operational translation signaled nonempirical elements (hence scientifically suspect and improper elements) within the theory.

We have seen how "being empirical" has a narrow and a broad meaning. Galileo was not an empiricist in any narrow sense; his *métier* was not the constant reiteration of accurate tests, statistical summaries, and probability parameters, precise experimental design, and an elaborate theory of errors. Yet, in the broad sense — the sense that identifies an empiricist as anyone who tells the *truth* about matters of physical fact because that alone is his objective — Galileo *was* an empiricist. He did not *invent* nature's properties in an act of divine geometrical creativity. Rather, he discerned profound analogies between mathematical analysis and analytical mechanics. Thus he articulated the dynamical facts as no one ever had before.

Similarly there may be a narrow and a broad interpretation of *the operational criterion of meaning*. In classical gravitation theory, F could never be set off against a list of physical operations from a consideration of which the real meaning of F would emerge. Gravitational forces cannot be cut, mechanically amplified, focused, insulated against, or modulated by, frequency controls. Our evidence in support of F is precisely what made us "invent" F to begin with! The *stress tensor* of general relativity (a replacement for F) fares little better in terms of strict and unrelieved operationalism. That is, its physical significance — its extrageometrical interpretation — is far from unambiguous. Moreover, the physical meaning of $\sqrt{-1}$ (as in commutation relations), of Schrödinger's ψ function, and Dirac's δ function (as in contemporary microphysics) — these also are somewhat suspect in rigorously operational terms. Such expressions cannot be "cashed" into observational currency, not without much philosophical advocacy of one rendition as against others.

What does this matter, however? In less direct ways, stress tensors, i, ψ, and δ, allow us to tell the truth about regions of the natural world as puzzling, intricate, and remote from ourselves as were *inertia* and *acceleration* puzzling for, and remote from, Galileo. Yet this great man, by invoking apparently nonempirical ideas like *limits, infinities,* and *instants,* was able to discover for us the essence of dynamical events. What better test for their legitimate use in physics? Similarly, the "bewilderness" of symbols which tumble out of pure function theory into our partial, nonlinear differential equations today—these are often, through near-interminable chains of intricate inference, ultimately descriptive of physical facts. What better test for their operational utility? We do not insist that automobile parts themselves be tiny automobiles, nor do we require that houses be made up of bricks and beams which are themselves small homes. Why then demand of entire physical theories — which, as a whole, should be operationally responsible — why demand that each component of such theories also be operationally interpretable, and in the same way? Words are not small sentences; cries are not petite prepositions; theoretical terms are not tiny theories. Demanding the full operational significance of δ is like demanding whether "the" is true or false.

We return full circle here to the vision of Galileo — perhaps now clearer for us than it could have been for him. "Telling the truth" about nature requires telling the whole truth and nothing but the truth; it requires, that is, a comprehensive explanatory account of a subject matter, no part of which is factually false. This consists in more than reciting tiny correlations and stuttering streams of statistical data. Galileo told the truths of dynamics through the languages of mathematical analysis; his objective justified his choice of technique. Had that objective been unattained — had he failed to tell the truth while yet continuing to press mathematics upon nature — then we could, and should, dub him "nonempirical."[33] Galileo's attunement of simple examples and pellucid mathematics to the then-obscure facts of dynamics, this was always effected with the sureness of a virtuoso. He was the conceptual master of nature, and his techniques were masterfully employed.

[33]In this sense LePlay's *Social Mechanics* was nonempirical.

So too ψ and δ can be masterfully employed in telling the truth about microphysical nature. Not directly observational, perhaps, but they remain indispensably inferential. Hence they are operationally respectable conceptions in just the way that Galileo was himself empirically respectable. This does *not* mean that the theoretical terms of modern physics are operationally tractable in the narrow sense of Mach and Ostwald; nor does it mean that Galileo was an empiricist in the narrow sense of Locke and Mill.

The Doctrine of Operationalism, then, needs lubrication and rejointing, as do the "received" views of Galileo's empirical discoveries in dynamics. For, so far as facts in the history of physical science are concerned, extremism in defense of a philosophy is no virtue.

4

EDWARD W. STRONG

GALILEO ON MEASUREMENT

"If a distinction cannot be made in language it cannot be made conceptually."[1] The language of an exact physical science is mathematical language — a language in which numbers are used to measure qualities. Intensive qualities such as temperature are measurable nonadditively in an order of numerical magnitudes arrayed as positions of degree on a scale. Extensive qualities such as space, time, and mass are measurable additively. Working with additive qualities of time and length, an investigator becomes able to establish precise quantitative relations between properties of bodies, for example, rate as a ratio between distance traversed and the time taken to traverse it.

In Galileo's scientific investigations, as in Newton's, a criterion of a theory is that it provides for measurable and

[1] E. A. Hanson, *Patterns of Discovery, An Inquiry into the Conceptual Foundations of Science* (Cambridge, 1958), p. 34.

Hanson calls attention to the distinction between "practical limitations" in forming a concept in a language in which it is not easily expressed and "logical limitations" in forming a concept in a language so structured as explicitly to forbid the formation (36, ftn. 2). Galileo commands the tool of Euclidean geometry in dealing with problems of motion — a tool suited to demonstration in terms of ratios and proportions but not for processes of integration and differentiation as later supplied by the invention of the calculus.

calculable consequences or conclusions testable against precise observations. Whatever is measurable can in principle be handled mathematically. " In mathematics," Newton writes, "we are to investigate the quantities of forces with their proportions consequent upon any conditions supposed; then, when we enter upon physics, we compare those proportions with the phenomena of nature, that we may know what conditions of those forces answer to the several kinds of attractive bodies. And this preparation being made, we argue more safely concerning the physical species, causes, and proportions of the forces."[2] Newton asserts that the whole burden of natural philosophy seems to consist in this — "from the phenomena of motions to investigate the forces of nature, and then from these forces to demonstrate other phenomena." Demonstration by mathematical reasoning is from "the laws and measures of gravity and other forces." Appropriately and essentially, then, rules of measure are stipulated in Newton's definitions of mass and momentum in the *Principia*:

Def. I. The Quantity of matter is the measure of the same, arising from its density and bulk conjointly.

Def. II. The Quantity of motion is the measure of the same, arising from the velocity and quantity of matter conjointly.

Fundamental to the attack of both Galileo and Newton on physical problems of motion are their concepts of measurable space, time, and mass.[3]

[2]*Sir Isaac Newton's Mathematical Principles of Natural Philosophy*, translated by Florian Cajori (Berkeley, 1934), Preface.

[3]L. W. H. Hull, *History and Philosophy of Science, an Introduction* (London, New York, and Toronto, 1934), p. 168. In discussing physical sciences in the seventeenth century, Hull stresses the demand that had emerged for theories "whose measurable consequences could

The inclined-plane experiment performed by Galileo in confirming the odd-number rule of acceleration of freely falling bodies exhibits how he measured to establish proportioning relations. He marked off units of length along a channel to measure distances traversed in the descent of a ball. For the measurement of time he provided for an equable flow of water collected in a glass and then weighed on a very accurate balance. In various timing trials with various inclinations of the plane and points of release of the ball, he reports that "the differences and ratios of these weights gave us the differences and ratios of the times, and this with such accuracy that although the operation was repeated many, many times, there was no appreciable discrepancy in the results." In repeated trials, "we always found that the spaces traversed were to each other as the squares of the times, and this was true for all inclinations of the plane, i. e., of the channel along which we rolled the ball."[4]

Thomas B. Settle,[5] in reproducing this experiment and in obtaining Galileo's reported results from it, points out that Galileo "had neither the apparatus of functional mathematics nor the interdefined system of standard weights and

---

be calculated, and their agreement with minute observation tested." (P. 162.) He points out that Newton's basic concepts are set forth in terms of measures, e.g., his second law of motion "decides how force is to be measured: it gives a quantitative definition." (P. 166.) See also E. W. Strong, "Newton's 'Mathematical Way,'" in *Roots of Scientific Thought*, edited by P. P. Wiener and A. Noland (New York, 1957), pp. 412–432.

[4]*Dialogues Concerning Two New Sciences*, H. Crew and A. de Salvio, translators (New York, 1914), p. 179.

[5]*Science*, January 6, 1961, Vol. 133, No. 3445, "An Experiment in the History of Science," pp. 19–23.

measures which would allow him to work with such a formula as $s = \frac{1}{2}gt^2$." Galileo's language was the language of Euclidean geometry. In working entirely with ratios, he had no need in this experiment for a system of standardized measures, but needed only to employ measures used consistently. Since rotational inertia was a constant in the experiment with respect to the ratio of vertical height of fall to a given slope length, the proportionalities obtained in proof of the law were not affected by the fact that Galileo did not take rotational inertia into account.

I

Physical operations of measurement fall in the domain of applied and not of pure mathematics. Galileo accords with the rationale of immediate predecessors in Italy in distinguishing "pure," "abstract," "contemplative," or "speculative" mathematical reasoning from "applied" mathematics. This rationale is set forth by Niccolo Tartaglia (1505–1557). Arithmetic and geometry are called "speculative" disciplines in that their logic of demonstration does not require knowledge gained through experience of physical things and operations. In his book on Euclid, Tartaglia commends these two disciplines to all scholars who seek knowledge and wisdom on the grounds that they "do not require any preliminary science to understand them" and that all other sciences and mechanical arts need mathematics. "It is a known fact that by means of these sciences or disciplines we recognize in natural happenings and in materials the descriptions, quality, and quantity of all geometrical forms. . . ." The properties and proportions of these forms, he continues, are "geometrically described and illustrated by our Author Euclide in fifteen volumes, of which eleven are of geometry . . . while three deal with Arithmetic. . . . The fifth pertains to all the others, dealing with proportions and proportionalities, therefore, the number and measure coincide."

A measure in the sense of a geometrical ratio or proportion of physical properties of bodies to which numbers are assigned requires the construction and employment of physical measuring instruments. Construction made on or in materials "can never be so true and exact but that it can always be made more true and exact." As a purely rational discipline, geometry does not consider triangles and circles in relation to physical bodies. Such a discipline is then distinguished from a science that is mathematical-physical: "The naturalist differs from the mathematician in that he considers things clothed, whereas the mathematician considers them as bare of any visible material."[6] This differentiation is credited by Tartaglia to Aristotle. As we will see, Galileo makes the same distinction.

A scientist moves from pure mathematics to applications not by abandoning demonstration but in proceeding to construction of measuring instruments and their employment in solving physical problems. Tartaglia makes this clear in defending his investigations in artillery:

And although the speaking of artillery and the firing of it, is not a thing very honorable in itself yet, since it is a new

[6]*Euclide Megarense acutissimo philosopho, solo introduttore delle scientie mathematice* (Venetia, Giovanni Bariletto, 1569), "First Lesson," Secs. 2–5.

For my exposition and commentary on the relation of "speculative" geometry to practical geometry and to the use of mathematics in physical sciences, as this relation is conceived and set forth by mathematicians in Italy and France prior to Galileo's work, see *Procedures and Metaphysics, A Study in the Philosophy of Mathematical-Physical Science in the Sixteenth and Seventeenth Centuries* (Berkeley, 1936), Chapters III–IV, pp. 47–113.

matter and not barren of speculation, I thought well to say a little on it, and in connexion with that subject, I am at present bringing out two sorts of instruments belonging to the art, that is to say, a square to regulate the discharging of said artillery, and also to level and examine every elevation. Also, another instrument for the investigation of distances on a plane surface, the description of which instruments will be published with my said work on artillery.[7]

The use of such instruments can yield not only precise quantifications but may also, in experiments performed, provide confirmations of functional correlations expressed as a law of physical phenomena. Galileo so casts experimentation, that is, in the role of confirming rather than of discovering laws. He is concerned with theoretical results. The practical geometers of the sixteenth and seventeenth

[7]Tartaglia's defense is made in reply to a letter from Cardan dated February 12, 1539, in which the latter takes Tartaglia to task for a "manifest error" in his book, *The New Science of Artillery*, in asserting, "at the fifth proposition of the first book, that no body of uniform weight can traverse any space of time or place by natural and violent motions mixed together; which is false, and contrary to all reason and natural experience. . . ."

In *Procedures and Metaphysics* (p. 88), I commented that "Tartaglia's reply on February 18 does not meet Cardan's justified objection to the Fifth Proposition (that a body could not move under the influence of transmitted force and the force of gravitation at the same time), but it illustrates beautifully that a mistake in principle does not deter the making of instruments and the determinations of measurement. Without determinations of measurement, debate on principles can go on without ever leading to an exact science of artillery. Cardan's observation upon the mixed motion in throwing a stone supports his objection to Tartaglia's separation of natural from violent motion, but does not supply demonstrated laws of trajectory." The two letters are published in *Quesiti et Inventioni Diverse* (Venetia, Venturino Ruffinelli, MDXLVI), Libro IX, pp. 117, 119; and in English translation in Henry Morley, *Jerome Cardan* (London, 1854; 2 vols.), I, p. 233, pp. 238-239.

centuries are concerned with practical applications. The attention they devote to the art of measuring is aimed at a general, exact practice and hence emphasizes design and employment of accurate, efficient measuring instruments for calculations. These geometers also insist on knowledge of Euclid's *Elements*, a knowledge required for following and employing methods of triangulation, projection, squaring, and proportioning. Although practical application of Euclid's geometry is the concern of Tartaglia's contemporary, Girolamo Cataneo, he also, in his book *On the Art of Measuring*, takes cognizance of mathematical proofs of physical propositions.

> And although the definitions and principles of geometry are intelligibles, abstracted from the senses, nevertheless they still fit in with geometry, perspective, mechanics, and natural philosophy; and by means of them, these propositions are proved in each of these sciences wherein one treats of size, figure, lines, surfaces, bodies subject to motion, and other perceptible matter, as is clearly seen not only in infinite places in Aristotle but also in other philosophers. Now if the other sciences utilize the principles of contemplative geometry, how much more would it be allowed to use them in this work of practical geometry?[8]

[8]*Dell' arte del misuare libri due, nel primo de' quali s'insegna a misuare, et partir i campi* (Brescia, P. M. Marchetti, 1548), Libro Primo, "Proemia della presente opera," p. 4. Cataneo explains that the geometer in "abstract" geometry, "conceives only in line, surface, and solid . . . conceives very differently from the astronomer, perspectivist, and natural philosopher." The astronomer considers celestial bodies in their greatness and movement, treating of them in amount. "The perspectivist treats of lines, surfaces, and bodies and of their accidents, to the extent that they fall under vision; but with mathematical proofs. The natural philosopher considers all things in the way in which they possess being or existence, in their own perceptible matter; but the geometrician knows this differently from

II

The consideration of geometrical forms clothed in material gives rise to the problem faced by Galileo — the problem of how demonstration in the abstract holds in the concrete. He confronts the problem in his comment on the proposition that equal weights in a balance of equal arms are in equilibrium, from which the general conclusion is derived that "any two heavy bodies are in equilibrium at distances which are inversely proportional to their weights."

This principle established, I desire, before passing to any other subject, to call your attention to the fact that these forces, resistances, moments, figures, etc., may be considered either in the abstract, disassociated from matter, or in the concrete, associated with matter. Hence the properties which belong to figures that are merely geometrical and non-material must be modified when we fill these figures with material and give them weight. . . . Hence before going further let us agree to distinguish between these two points of view; when we consider an instrument in the abstract, i. e., apart from the weight of its own material, we shall speak of "taking it in an absolute sense" [*prendere assolutamente*]; but if we fill one of these simple and absolute figures with matter and thus give it weight, we shall refer to such a material figure as a "moment" or "compound force" [*momento o forza composta*].[9]

As concerns questions of "how much?" or "how many?" or "how many times?" in the filling or clothing of mathe-

---

each of the above mentioned; in this respect he differentiates things which he considers by his intellect from perceptible matter, from movement and from any alteration; where the existence of quantity is indeed in natural bodies, nevertheless, he considers it with his intellect without material, without perceptible accidents."

[9]*Two New Sciences*, pp. 112–113.

matical figures and diagrams, the questions are answerable only by physical measurements. When an "absolute" demonstration does not answer to quantified physical properties, the deficiency may be attributable either to faulty conceptualization or to limitations of mathematical tools available — limitations which in turn may cramp or misdirect conceptualization. A third possibility of error lies, of course, in inaccurate measurements and the calculation based on them. In investigating concomitant variation of one quantity in relation to variation of another, Galileo's physical experimentation is designed to provide measures, and measurements made in turn enable him to formulate precise definitions and descriptions or to state problems and solutions in terms of exact quantities.

Galileo's fourteenth-century predecessors in physics were blind to the necessity of measuring concomitant variations in establishing and testing laws of motion.[10] Galileo was not. He opens the discussion of "Naturally Accelerated Motion" in the *Two New Sciences* by remarking:

> The properties belonging to uniform motion have been discussed in the preceding section; but accelerated motion remains to be considered. And first of all it seems desirable to find and explain a definition best fitting natural phenomena. For anyone may invent an arbitrary type of

[10]A. C. Crombie states that fourteenth-century scholars who worked out kinematic theorems for motions "displayed no interest in finding means to apply their results to actual motions. They went through the whole discussion without making a single measurement, although leading scholars like Bradwardine and Albert of Saxony were looking for the true laws of motion, and although they formulated their laws in such a way that they could find the answer only by measuring concomitant variations in the parameters involved." ("The Significance of Medieval Discussions of Scientific Method for the Scientific Revolution," in *Critical Problems in the History of Science*, ed. by Marshall Clagett, University of Wisconsin Press, Madison, 1959, p. 92.)

motion and discuss its properties; . . . but we have decided to consider the phenomena of bodies falling with an acceleration such as actually occurs in nature and to make this definition of accelerated motion exhibit the essential features of observed accelerated motions.[11]

The question I shall now explore concerns Galileo's views on measurement. What role does he assign to mensuration in establishing laws in an exact science? A first point of major importance to be taken up is introduced by Newton in his assertion that geometry, founded in mechanical practice, "is that part of universal mechanics which accurately proposes and demonstrates the art of measuring."[12] Measurements of the kind made by Galileo in the inclined-plane experiment yield quantifications of spaces traversed in intervals of time. This does not ensure correct conceptualization and thereby correct utilization of experimental results in the sensible measures obtained. One may accurately demonstrate, in the sense of reasoning with precise amounts without logical error, and yet reason from false premises or postulates. Galileo measured aright for the task he undertook seeking an experimental confirmation of a law of acceleration he already believed to be true and mathematically demonstrable. He accurately proposed not merely in the sense that his physical measurements were sufficiently refined and precise to yield numbers on which he could rely in further mathematical reasoning. He accurately proposed in having arrived at a correct conceptual formulation after he had earlier adopted an erroneous one. As N. R. Hanson points out, "Galileo's error consists in this: the principle he adopts as evident and natural — that the velocities of freely falling bodies are proportional to

11*Two New Sciences*, p. 160.
12*Principia*, Preface.

the distances travelled — could never lead to the law of falling bodies as he formulated it. It leads to an entirely different law, expressible only as an exponential function. Galileo could never have managed such a formulation with the mathematics at his disposal." Hanson then asks why it took Galileo so long a time to discover his mistake and to arrive at a correct statement of the principle, namely, that "the velocities of a freely falling body are proportional to the times — not to the distances."[13]

One of the hampering factors to which Hanson calls attention appears to be lodged in the spatial notation of Euclidean geometry. In deciding to treat motion geometrically, Galileo set aside his earlier effort of trying to account for motion by impetus imparted to bodies. His triangular representation of augments of velocity in relation to distances traversed, Hanson observes, "allows one only to set out this uniform increase in relation to time. The notation blinds Galileo to this. He transfers to space what belongs to time," i.e., he plots velocities against distances and not against times.[14] Thus Galileo, in his letter to Paolo Sarpi in 1604, postulates as a fundamental principle that "the velocity of a freely falling body increases in proportion to the distance it has fallen from its starting point."

Galileo does not inform us how he discovered this earlier error to rectify it later. In opening up the subject of "Naturally Accelerated Motion" in the *Two New Sciences*, he first defines uniformly accelerated motion: "A motion is said to be uniformly accelerated when, starting from rest, it acquires during equal time intervals, equal increments of speed." In the ensuing discussion, Sagredo remarks that "the definition

---

[13]*Patterns of Discovery, an Inquiry into the Conceptual Foundations of Science* (Cambridge, 1958), p. 38.

[14]*Patterns of Discovery*, p. 43.

might have been put a little more clearly without changing the fundamental idea — namely, uniformly accelerated motion is such that its speed increases in proportion to spaces traversed." Salviati replies, "It is very comforting to me to have had such a companion in error; and moreover let me tell you that your proposition seems so highly probable that our Author himself admitted, when I advanced this opinion to him, that he had for some time shared the same fallacy." Simplicio is not convinced that there is a fallacy. "I am one of those who accepts the proposition, and I believe that a falling body acquires force [*vires*] in its descent, its velocity increasing in proportion to the space, and that the momentum [*momento*] of the falling body is doubled when it falls from a doubled height; . . ." Salviati then demonstrates the falsity of the two propositions, in each instance with a concluding confirmation based on what "observation shows."[15]

Did Galileo's measurements of time intervals in the inclined-plane experiment not only provide for precise formulations of ratios but also lead him to discover his earlier mistake in rectifying it? This is possible, but this is not how he portrays the experiment. As concerns a demonstration of the odd-number rule, "once having accepted the definition of uniformly accelerated motion," the question at issue is this. Is the theoretically asserted acceleration that which one meets in nature in bodies freely falling from a

15*Two New Sciences*, p. 162, pp. 167–168. Sagredo's immediate response to the definition of uniformly accelerated motion is a comment on definitions as nominal. "Although I can offer no rational objection to this or indeed any other definition, devised by any author whomsoever, since all definitions are arbitrary, I may nevertheless without offense be allowed to doubt whether such a definition as the above, established in an abstract manner, corresponds to and describes that kind of accelerated motion which we meet in nature in the case of freely falling bodies."

point of rest? An experiment is requested to substantiate a conclusion laid down in advance, namely, that the spaces traversed are in the ratio of the square of the times. Such a request is said to be a very reasonable one, "in those sciences where mathematical demonstrations are applied to natural phenomena, as is seen in the case of perspective, astronomy, mechanics, music, and others where the principles, once established by well-chosen experiments, become the foundations of the entire superstructure." Galileo does not say that the principles are discovered by experiments, although they might be so discovered, but only that well-chosen experiments establish the principles. "So far as experiments go, they have not been neglected by the Author; and often in his company, I have attempted in the following manner to assure myself that the acceleration actually experienced by falling bodies is that above described."

Although Galileo does not inform us that he hit upon the law of squares by the experiment he performed and the measurements he made, he did obtain a confirmation of a theoretical description. He discovered experimentally that acceleration "actually experienced" fitted the law and thereby confirmed that it had predictive value. He could never have been assured of this without physical measurements verifying a relation asserted by the law, irrespective of whether or not he first hit upon the law independent of any experimentation.

III

If we look further into Galileo's treatment of "compound motion" in the *Two New Sciences*, the question arises as to how one is to overcome difficulties and objections standing in the way of arriving at fixed laws and exact descriptions when perturbations of a resistant medium and other physical complications raise doubts about the application in concrete of conclusions proved in the abstract. Theorem I, Proposition I, states that "A projectile which is carried by a uniform horizontal motion compounded with a naturally accelerated physical motion describes a path which is a semi-parabola." The downward motion accelerated in pro-proportion to the square of the times is motion toward the center of the earth. The horizontal motion of the projectile is supposed to be on a plane. From the point of discharge, then, the ball flies on a tangent each point of which would depart farther and farther from the center of the earth if the horizontal motion were not compounded with the ver-tical motion. Apart from the resistance of the medium, how is it permissible to assume that the motion will remain uni-form on the horizontal plane? Galileo asserts that "any velocity once imparted to a moving body will be rigidly maintained as long as the external causes of acceleration or retardation are removed, a condition which is found only on horizontal planes . . . from this it follows that motion along a horizontal plane is perpetual; for, if the velocity be uniform, it cannot be diminished or slackened, much less destroyed."[16] The concept of inertia is here grasped in terms of eliminating or abstracting from accelerating or retarding causes. Newton also conceptualizes the principle by ab-stracting in stating that "Every body continues in its state of rest, or of uniform motion in a right line, unless it is compelled to change that state by forces impressed on it."

Galileo concedes that, in the concrete, the horizontal mo-tion will not be uniform. It does not follow from this con-

---

[16]*Two New Sciences*, p. 215. See E. J. Dijksterhuis, *The Mechaniza-tion of the World Picture* (Oxford, 1961), pp. 347–353, concerning Galileo's conception of inertia as a tendency to persevere in circular motion.

cession, however, that we are not entitled to "take for granted" that the beam of a balance or steelyard is a straight line, "every point of which is equidistant from the common center of all heavy bodies, and that the cords by which the heavy bodies are suspended are parallel to each other." Yet were the cords from which the bodies are suspended at each end of the beam extended from the circumference of the earth to its center, the figure formed would be an isosceles triangle. Faced with this problem, Galileo writes: "Some consider this assumption permissible because, in practice, our instruments and the distances are so small in comparison with the enormous distance from the center of the earth that we may consider a minute of arc on a great circle as a straight line, and may regard the perpendiculars let fall from its extremities as parallel." An architect, Galileo remarks, is not in practical difficulty in using a plumb line to erect high towers with parallel sides. This observation, however, does not meet the point at issue. What is permissible when, from our instrumental determinations, we formulate ratios or functions in law statements? One way of escape from difficulties introduced by confronting a mathematical demonstration with physical complications is indicated by Galileo: "I may add that, in all their discussions, Archimedes and the others considered themselves as located at an infinite distance from the center of the earth, in which case their assumptions were not false, and therefore their conclusions were absolutely correct." Galileo, however, does not assume an infinitely extended empty space. Rather, he asserts, "When we wish to apply our proven conclusions to distances which, though finite, are very large, it is necessary for us to infer, on the basis of demonstrated truth, what correction is to be made for the fact that our distance from the center of the earth is not really infinite, but merely very great in comparison with the small dimensions of our apparatus." In a firing range of four miles in which paths of cannon balls terminate on the earth's surface, "only very slight changes can take place in their parabolic figure which, it is conceded, would be greatly altered if they terminated at the center of the earth."

As to the perturbation arising from the resistance of the medium, Galileo remarks that "this is more considerable and does not, on account of its manifold forms, submit to fixed laws and exact description. . . . Even horizontal motion which, if no impediment were offered, would be uniform and constant is altered by the resistance of the air and finally ceases; and here again the less dense [*più leggerio*] the body the quicker the process." The way out of the difficulty is methodological:

In order to handle this matter in a scientific way, it is necessary to cut loose from these difficulties; and having discovered and demonstrated the theorems in the case of no resistance, to use and apply them with such limitations as experience will teach. And the advantage of this method will not be small; for the material and shape of the projectile may be chosen as dense and round as possible, so that it will encounter the least resistance in the medium, nor will the spaces and velocities in general be so great but that we shall easily be able to correct them with precision.[17]

Galileo proceeds to argue that, in the case of projectiles used,

. . .the deviation from an exact parabolic path is quite insensible. Indeed, if you will allow me a little greater liberty, I can show you, by two experiments, that the dimensions of our apparatus are so small that these external and incidental resistances, among which that of

[17]*Ibid.*, pp. 252–253.

the medium is the most considerable, are scarcely observable.

The second experiment counts the vibrations of two equal leaden balls suspended from two threads of equal length. The first pendulum is swung 80 degrees or more from the perpendicular and the second only 4 or 5 degrees. Counting the vibrations of each, they will be found not to differ by a single vibration.

> This observation justifies the two following propositions, namely, that vibrations of very large and very small amplitude all occupy the same time and that the resistance of the air does not affect motions of high speed more than those of low speed, contrary to the opinion hitherto generally entertained.[18]

The respects in which an assumption of the abstract or theoretical kind under discussion is permissible, even though not absolutely correct in physical application, can now be summarized:

1. An assumption is permissible when, in practice and for practice, the errors or deviations are either so small as to be negligible or are correctible with precision or by approximations.

2. An assumption is permissible when, postulating an ideal or abstract frame of reference from which mathematically correct conclusions have been drawn, one or another method of measuring can be employed which provides calculations by which to confirm or disconfirm the conclusions.

Galileo's postulates are Euclidean in form. They guide and control the design of the experiments and the conduct of mensuration. Demonstration through the use of geo-

18*Ibid.*, p. 255.

metrical diagrams and proportions, to be conclusive in the concrete as well as the abstract, requires of the investigator that he be able to supply physical measures to establish relations. Two passages in the *Dialogue Concerning the Two Chief World Systems* are pertinent here. The first has to do with the general knowledge that freely falling bodies starting from rest are continually accelerated. "But this general knowledge is of no value unless one knows the ratio according to which the increase in speed takes place." The odd-number rule is then stated, "the spaces passed over are to each other as the square of the times," followed by the assertion that there is a "purely mathematical proof" of this.[19] The question that can then be raised occurs a few pages earlier. Simplicio objects to a mathematical demonstration (which, in the application Galileo made of it, is indeed erroneous) as follows: "After all, Salviati, these mathematical subtleties do very well in the abstract, but they do not work out when applied to sensible and physical matters. For instance, mathematicians may prove well enough in theory that *sphaera tangit planum in puncto*, a proposition similar to the one in hand; but when it comes to matter, things happen otherwise. What I mean about these angles of contact and ratios is that they all go by the board for material and sensible things." Salviati replies that the mathematical scientist [*filosofo geometra*], "when he wants to recognize in the concrete the effects which he has proved in the abstract, must deduct the material hindrances, and if he is able to do so, I assure you that things are in no less agreement than arithmetical computations. The errors, then, lie not in the abstractness or concreteness, not in geometry

· 19*Dialogue Concerning the Two Chief World Systems*, translated with revised notes by Stillman Drake (University of California Press, 1962), pp. 221–222.

or physics, but in a calculator who does not know how to make a true accounting. Hence if you had a perfect sphere and a perfect plane, even though they were material, you would have no doubt that they touched in one point; . . ."[20]

Were the elimination of hindrances by the mathematical scientist such that he invented an arbitrary scheme of relations inapplicable for lack of physical mensuration, his decision to do so would be contrary to that announced by Galileo. For, to repeat a statement earlier cited: "but we have decided to consider the phenomena of bodies falling with an acceleration such as actually occurs in nature and to make this definition of accelerated motion exhibit the essential features of observed accelerated motions." For Galileo, a true accounting of physical phenomena must be more than just purely mathematical. He recounts, for example, his own efforts to determine the true from the apparent angular diameter of fixed stars. He hopes to find some observable alterations "by which it might be discovered what the annual motion [of the earth] does reside in. Then they, too, no less than the planets and the sun itself, would appear in court to give witness to such motion in favor of the earth. For I do not believe that the stars are spread over a spherical surface at equal distances from one center; . . ."[21]

For an observer carried by the earth in annual motion, both variations in apparent size and differences in elevation would, if they could be perceived on the basis of approach and retreat, afford the evidence sought. Galileo gives cogent reasons why such variation has not, as yet, been perceived:

It is possible, Copernicus declares, that the immense distance of the starry sphere makes such small phenomena unobservable. And as had already been remarked, it may

[20]*Ibid.*, p. 203, pp. 207–208.
[21]*Ibid.*, p. 382.

be that up to the present they have not even been looked for, or if looked for, not sought out in such a way as they need to be; that is, with all necessary precision and minute accuracy. It is hard to achieve this precision, both on account of the imperfection of astronomical instruments, which are subject to much variation, and because of the shortcomings of those who handle them with less care than is required. . . . As a matter of fact, how would you expect anyone to be sure, with a quadrant or sextant that customarily has an arm three or four yards long, that he is not out by two or three minutes in the setting of the perpendicular or the alignment of the alidade? . . . Besides which, it is almost impossible for the instrument to be constructed absolutely accurate and then maintained so.[22]

Galileo expresses his desire to have far larger and more precise observing and measuring instruments. "And if in the course of these operations any such variation shall happen to become known, how great an achievement will be made in astronomy! For by this means, besides ascertaining the annual motion, we shall be able to gain a knowledge of the size and distance of that same star."[23]

In view of Galileo's expression of need for more precise instruments and of desirability of having them be made and maintained as accurate as possible, one would expect him to advocate a common standard of measure. This expectation is fulfilled in the *Two New Sciences*. The request is made to show how, in the case of two uniform motions, one horizontal and the other perpendicular, one obtains the resultant from the components.

Salviati replies:

Your request is altogether reasonable and I will see whether my long consideration of these matters will en-

22*Ibid.*, p. 387.
23*Ibid.*, p. 389.

able me to make them clear to you. But you must excuse me if in the explanation I repeat many things already said by the Author. Concerning motions and their velocities or momenta [*movimenti e lor velocità o impeti*] whether uniform or naturally accelerated, one cannot speak definitely until he has established a measure for such velocities and also for time. As for time we have the already widely adopted hours, first minutes, and second minutes. So for velocities, just as for intervals of time, there is need of a common standard which shall be understood and accepted by everyone, and which shall be the same for all. As has already been stated, the Author considers the velocity of a freely falling body adapted to this purpose, since this velocity increases according to the same law in all parts of the world; thus for instance the speed acquired by a leaden ball of a pound weight started from rest and falling vertically through the height of, say, a spear's length is the same in all places; it is therefore excellently adapted for representing the momentum [*impeto*] acquired in the case of natural fall.[24]

In proposing such a natural standard, Galileo turns next to discovering

> ... a method of measuring momentum in such a way that all who discuss the subject will form the same conception of its size and velocity [*grandezza e velocita*]. This will prevent one person from imagining it larger, another smaller, than it really is; so that in the composition of a given uniform motion with one which is accelerated men may not obtain different values for the resultant. In order to determine and represent such momentum and particular speed [*impeto e velocità particolarè*] our Author has found no better method than to use the momentum acquired by a body in naturally accelerated motion.

Galileo then seeks to make this clear by a particular example beginning,

[24]*Two New Sciences*, p. 264.

Let us consider the speed and momentum acquired by a body falling through the height, say, of a spear *[picca]* as a standard which we may use in the measurement of other speeds and momenta as occasion demands. . . .[25]

Galileo has not grasped what needs to be done to have a standard measure which shall be the same for all.[26] Unless measuring instruments are calibrated against a standard unit of measure and maintained in accurate condition, the results obtained by one measuring rod will not coincide with another measuring rod nor will later measurements by the same rod be invariable as related to earlier ones. Moreover, with respect to what is measured, we need either to be able to maintain standard conditions or to be able to correct the values obtained by a physical measurement, assuming that our measuring rod is itself a rigid body not subject to deformations. Galileo's natural common standard of measure depends on propositions about properties of bodies that are more than geometrical. They are physical and mechanical, such that they require empirical confirmation not obtainable without quantifications supplied by physical measurements. The reliability of these measurements in turn depends on maintained accuracy of standardized instruments and on skilled use of them.

Galileo is not going astray in seeking for natural constants to be employed in mensuration. He, like Robert Hooke after him, recognizes the need for and utility of common standards of measure. In concluding a report of two experiments, one on the pressure of water in pipes and the other

[25]*Ibid.*, pp. 264–265.

[26]Problems involved in ascribing numerical values to spatial magnitudes are discussed by Ernest Nagel, *The Structure of Science, Problems in the Logic of Scientific Explanation* (New York and Burlingame, 1961), pp. 254–267.

on the comparative expansion of any metal, fluid or solid, Hooke writes:

> The Reason of the making of which Experiment was, to hint the Necessity there is, in all Experiments fit to be made Use of for any Philosophical Theories, of reducing them to a Certainty of Quantity; without which, no certain and unquestionable conclusion can be made. Now tho' a certain Standard of Weight, Measure, Expansion, Power, Motion, &c. be not made Use of; yet if some one determinate Measure for each of them be pitched upon, 'twill be enough to make the comparative Trials useful; though it were to be wish'd, that some universal, natural Standard of Measure for all Things were found out, those that have hitherto been thought of, having been doubted of, as to their Universality and Certainty, at all Places and in all Times.[27]

A universal natural standard of measure is not discoverable in the absence of reliable determinate measures. Near the end of the *Two New Sciences,* Galileo takes up the subject of the blows or shocks of projectiles in striking a target. Sagredo remarks that no author has given a solution to the problem presented, that of discovering a method of measuring the force *[forza]* of such a percussion. "I can hardly think it infinite, but incline rather to the view that it has its limit and can be counterbalanced and measured by other forces, such as weights, or by levers or screws or other mechanical instruments which are used to multiply forces in a manner which I satisfactorily understand."[28] Salviati reports that he received great consolation from our Academician. "First he told me that he also had for a long time been

[27]*Philosophical Experiments and Observations of the Late Eminent Dr. Robert Hooke, F. R. S. and Geom. Prof. Gresh. and Other Eminent Virtuoso's in his Time* (London, MDCCXXVI), p. 95.

[28]*Two New Sciences,* p. 271.

groping in the dark; but later he said that, after having spent some thousands of hours in speculating and contemplating thereon, he had arrived at some notions which are far removed from our earlier ideas and which are remarkable for their novelty."

The promised explanation is postponed to a later day; but clearly Galileo recognizes that, besides the blows or shocks of projectiles, "we must add another very important consideration; to determine the force and energy of the shock *[forza ed energia della percossa]* it is not sufficient to consider only the speed of the projectiles, but we must also take into account the nature and condition of the target which, in no small degree, determines the efficiency of the blow."[29]

Here again the filling of abstract diagrams with matter brings home that physics is not merely mathematical, nor to be viewed as just a hypothetical-deductive system. For Galileo, Euclidean geometry provides a theoretical framework of mensuration, but such framework does not insure *a priori* that precision instruments employed in measurement will yield confirmations of conclusions reached by mathematical reasoning. Galileo aims at demonstration based on permissible assumptions concerning fundamental principles. When his conclusion that "in a medium totally devoid of resistance all bodies would fall with the same speed" is doubted, the confirming justification he supplies is reasoned from physical findings:

> Our problem is to find out what happens to bodies of different weight moving in a medium devoid of resistance, so that the only difference in speed is that which arises from inequality of weight. Since no medium except one entirely free from air and other bodies, be it ever so tenuous

[29]*Ibid.*, p. 269.

and yielding, can furnish our senses with the evidence we are looking for, and since such a medium is not available, we shall observe what happens in the rarest and least resistant media as compared with what happens in denser and more resistant media. Because if we find as a fact that the variation of speed among bodies of different specific gravities is less and less according as the medium becomes more and more yielding, and if finally in a medium of extreme tenuity, though not a perfect vacuum, we find that, in spite of great diversity of specific gravity [peso], the difference in speed is very small and almost inappreciable, we are then justified in believing it highly probable that in a vacuum all bodies would fall with the same speed.[30]

The science Galileo seeks to advance is exact science — a science in which he seeks to establish general numerical laws expressing invariable relations between physical properties and to connect these laws systematically. I have sought to call attention to Galileo's clear recognition that the search for general invariant laws requires quantifications of properties of bodies that can only be provided by mensuration.

[30]*Ibid.*, p. 72.

5

PHILIP H. ABELSON

SCIENCE AND GOVERNMENT

The modes of thought and behavior that Galileo exemplified led to unprecedented revolutions in human affairs. He was a key to the development of modern science and technology. It has even been suggested that he influenced the later development of democratic forms of government.

Galileo's contributions were not only in the discoveries he made but equally in his procedures in making them and in later working for their acceptance. In effect, Galileo discovered science. He demonstrated that a fruitful scientific investigation starts with a conflict between preconceived notions and a new experience, followed by a critical, searching analysis and the devising of crucial experiments. Once new insights were gained, Galileo was willing to engage in polemical exchanges to gain acceptance of his findings. Essential to his approach was a disregard, even a defiance, of human authority and established dogma. In this attitude Galileo overcame a deep-rooted human tendency. Nearly all human beings are mentally lazy. When a difficult problem arises we may worry at it for a while, but we sooner or later abandon the effort and are pleased to fall back on the dicta of an authority on the subject. Most men spend their lives learning and parroting the dogmas of their time. The greatness of civilization today rests on the fact that rare venturesome souls like Galileo were capable of rising above the usual pattern.

In the centuries before Galileo's time, human thought was largely dominated by dogma and authority. In the last several hundred years science and authority have been in conflict. The methods of science have been so powerful and creative that authority and dogma have often been forced to retreat. Nevertheless, the battle is one that science can never finally win. The deep-seated habits of mental laziness are too universal. The overwhelming majority wish to be told what to think.

In this conflict of science and authority, how goes the battle today? A casual examination would suggest that it goes well. The number of people called scientists has been increasing rapidly; their prestige is high. Indeed, a recent study has shown that the public accords a higher standing to scientists than to state governors or congressmen. At the same time scientific research is being subsidized on an unprecedented scale. Men trained in science are occupying important positions in government and in industry. During the past decade the conflict between science and authority has seemingly diminished. Authority has accepted research and development as desirable activities. In turn, large segments of science have joined the establishment. On the surface the relationship appears relatively sound. A deeper look presents a view that is not so reassuring.

The authority of the federal government has so risen that government has power transcending that of any other segment of society. Its power is growing and seems destined to continue to do so. At the same time the financial needs of science have been increasing. To obtain new knowledge requires expensive facilities, which are mainly financed by the government. Owing to financial dependence the fate of the burgeoning scientific establishment rests largely with the politicians and the federal establishment.

In this talk I shall develop the theme that politicians cannot be expected to understand science and are likely to use the weight of their position to attempt to direct science toward goals of their choosing. I will also consider some of the effects on science of the present concentration of federal support. Finally, I will suggest some measures that might be taken to ensure that the spirit of Galileo does not depart from American science.

The essence of science is foreign to politicians. By nature and by education they tend to be authoritarians. Most of them are trained as lawyers, whose basic approach is to honor precedent. In their approach to problems, politicians practice the "art of the possible." When truth is useful, it is employed. But when truth gets in the way, it may be edited. Moreover, in a democracy politicians must give great weight to the views of the majority. Now, it is a characteristic of science that progress is dependent on disregarding the views of even an overwhelming majority. At the time a new insight is gained, the discoverer is in fact a minority of one.

Congressional committees are willing to listen to scientists, and on occasion they invite scientific testimony. When they do so, however, they give real attention only to so-called authorities. I recall a congressional hearing involving a group of competent scientists whose lead-off witness was Edward Teller. While Teller testified, the full membership of the congressional committee listened, and a large contingent of the press busily took notes. When he finished, almost all the congressmen and the press departed. The remaining scientists had carefully prepared for their presentations, and their testimony was as important as Teller's. But, as far as affecting events was concerned, the group was wasting its time.

In relating this incident I am not seeking to criticize but rather to point out a reality. Most of us, if cast in the role of congressmen, would very likely act in much the same way. Faced with puzzling problems whose fundamentals we do not comprehend, we instinctively turn to authority. There literally is not time to acquire the knowledge and experience to deal at first hand with multiple complexities.

In considering the health of science and its relation to the federal government, there is another reality that should be recognized. Much of the public does not fully understand what science is all about. Politicians recognize that with knowledge comes a by-product, namely, power — power to control and change the environment, power to produce all manner of wealth, military power. They are impressed by these facets of power, but few seem interested in knowledge for itself. The present status of science stems from the effectiveness of hardware that resulted from scientific knowledge.

To an important degree the present affluence of science dates crucially from about twenty years ago. Many of the enterprises leading to great military developments during World War II were based on research at universities: for instance, the development of radar techniques in the Radiation Laboratory at M.I.T., the participation in atomic bomb work by Columbia University and the universities of California and Chicago, proximity fuse work by The Johns Hopkins University, and rocket propulsion at the California Institute of Technology. These fundamental programs all contributed crucial technological advances and were decisive in giving the nation advantages in weapons capabilities. The atomic bomb came late in the war and actually had less effect on the course of the conflict than some of the other developments. But the detonation at Hiroshima was so dramatic as to leave with the average man a profound impression of the power of science. All too soon the cold war began, and with it came the fear that an enemy might make important discoveries faster than we. Later, Sputnik intensified these fears. The stage was set for large-scale federal support of scientific research in this country. Congress also came to realize that important technological developments often rest on basic research and new knowledge. But to them research has been principally a tool with which to achieve an end. Usually when politicians speak of scientific research, they mean research in connection with development. For the most part the two words are coupled, and usually they are regarded as inseparable. In the text of the 1964 Democratic platform is a good illustration of how both parties stand in the matter. Under the heading of "Science" is to be found material of which the following is illustrative:

In the years 1961–1964, the United States has:

*Successfully flown the Saturn I rocket, putting into orbit the heaviest payloads of the space age to date.

*Moved rapidly forward with much more powerful launch vehicles, the Saturn IB and the Saturn V. . . .

*Mastered the difficult technology of using liquid hydrogen as a space rocket fuel in the Centaur upper stage rocket and the Saturn I second stage. . . .

*Successfully completed six manned space flights in Project Mercury, acquiring 54 hours of space flight experience.

*Successfully flight-tested the two-man Gemini space-craft and Titan II space rocket. . . .

In the words devoted to "Science" about a score of such examples of construction of hardware are cited. There is no direct reference to the creation of knowledge or mention of such advances as our progress in molecular biology. When politicians support research, they do so in the expectation that they are buying gadgets. When research has no obvious connection with development, it can become a target for criticism.

One of the most powerful members of Congress is Representative Howard W. Smith of Virginia, Chairman of the Committee on Rules. In the hearings that led to authorization of the Elliott Committee,[1] Mr. Smith expressed himself in a discussion of a List of Projects supported by the National Science Foundation.

> This book contains principally a list of all of the grants to colleges and students for scholarships to study specific things. . . .

> For instance, here is one to study shellfish in the vicinity of Venezuela and that costs the modest sum of $1,300. I suppose that was for a fishing trip. . . .

> We have one next to that for $5,000 for a couple of years' study to a university on the evolution of box turtles.

> I do not know what box turtles are but maybe they are a special variety that needs investigation. . . .

> Here is an interesting one for $64,000 to study resistance to persuasion.

[1]U.S. Congress, Hearings before the Committee on Rules, House of Representatives, 88th Congress, First Session, on House Resolution 455 and Companion Resolutions, August 13 and 15, 1963.

Some of us thought Adam and Eve had settled that question with the apple, but it seems like we have to go over the same ground again at a cost of $64,000.

Representative Smith was a little off base on that last item. He seems to have forgotten about brainwashed prisoners of the Korean War.

These comments are a sample of attitudes that were expressed by others during the hearings leading to the appointment of the Elliott Committee last fall. This investigating group was unanimously authorized in a move that indicated considerable underlying discontent with what the House considered a lack of an appropriate degree of control over federally supported research.

Recent events suggest that a further evolution of the relation of Congress and science is under way. Research and development funds are likely to become a great new pork barrel. Indeed, such a trend is becoming apparent. Some who have analyzed the policies of the space agency speak admiringly of Mr. Webb's political adroitness in allocating facilities. It should not be astonishing that such a tendency should appear. Perhaps the amazing fact is that research and development was not made a pork barrel earlier.

Congressmen have been impressed with the relation of Harvard and M.I.T. to the expanding electronics industry around Boston. They are also aware of the role that the California institutions have played in bringing vast defense industries to that state. They note a concentration of both federal research and development funds in a limited number of institutions and states. The federal budget of $15 billion for these purposes is obviously a powerful economic stimulant to the recipient regions.

Some of these views are outlined in the following excerpt

from the First Progress Report of the Elliott Committee (the Select Committee on Government Research of the House of Representatives):[2]

There is a growing feeling of concern that a more than generous share of the ... funds spent for applied research and for development is ... concentrated in a handful of States. It is clear that our national security must not be impaired by regional considerations in research and development expenditures; it is equally clear that, to an extent perhaps not yet accurately measurable, these same expenditures have an extraordinarily powerful impact on the educational, industrial, and employment sectors of every region's vitality.

A key factor in the changing congressional attitude has been the influence of members of the Joint Committee on Atomic Energy. In a recent article in *Science*,[3] Senator Anderson expressed some of the attitudes of a veteran influential member of the Joint Committee:

In the last analysis it is the collective wisdom of Congress itself which counts most in making important decisions. No decisions can be made in isolation, on a completely scientific basis, by disinterested officials. Congress will consider the scientific aspects of a proposal and pay attention to the facts assembled by the engineer. But in addition, Congressmen must ask some further questions: What will the impact be on our economy? What effect will the proposal have on our foreign relations? Will it contribute to the health and welface of the nation?

[2]U.S. Congress, Federal Research and Development Programs, First Progress Report of the Select Committee on Government Research of the House of Representatives, 88th Congress, Second Session, p. 8, February 17, 1964.

[3]Clinton P. Anderson, "Scientific advice for Congress," *Science*, Vol. 144, No. 3614, p. 31, April 3, 1964.

There are numerous examples from the area of atomic energy when Congress spurred momentous decisions, in the face of inconclusive advice from experts, which have withstood the challenge of history and have proved right.

In a recent speech[4] another member of the Joint Committee, Representative Price, goes further. He indicates a belief that Congress should actively enter into the management of government-supported research and development. In this speech he outlined "some of the principles which I believe Congress should establish during this period of very careful re-examination of Federal research and development activities. The points of concern to Congress will include:

First, establishment of clear-cut objectives for research and development projects.

Second, a realistic cost estimate for the entire project: not just the immediate year.

Third, centralized responsibility and continuity of management.

Fourth, a plan to follow through; to put the results of research and development to actual use.

Congressman Price also pointed to high-energy physics as an area that might be subjected to the examination he had outlined. Mr. Price's four major points are applicable to many activities supported by the government, such as developments of weapons or most of the space program. They also seem applicable to research carried out in connection with such development work. High-energy physics, however, though costly, is in another category. The magnitude of the funds required, of course, makes some planning essential, but how can a cost estimate be made for the discovery

---

[4]"A new era in government research and development," remarks by Congressman Melvin Price, Chairman of Subcommittee on Research, Development, and Radiation, Press Release No. 459 of Joint Committee on Atomic Energy, U.S. Congress, September 14, 1964.

of a particle that hasn't been discovered yet? If these principles are to be applied to high-energy physics, are they not also applicable elsewhere? Should not the biologists be required to estimate the cost of completely elucidating the genetic code or of identifying the chain of electron donors and acceptors in photosynthesis? Once the precedent of congressional planning of research were established, the practice might be carried to ridiculous lengths. I am loath to believe that this will happen soon, but the possibility of restrictive congressional controls cannot be dismissed.

In a few research projects, such as in high-energy physics, congressional committees may become closely involved. But, for the most part, controls are likely to be applied through the granting agencies, which of necessity are closely attuned to the wishes of Congress. These agencies are mainly staffed by men who have been trained in science and find themselves in a difficult role. They are at the interface of two different worlds, and neither world fully trusts or honors them. As the science administrators have considerable voice in policies and in determining who is supported, it is desirable to understand their backgrounds and attitudes toward creative science.

To understand the mature scientist, let us consider his development. After embryonic scientists have become deeply committed, they often find that research is not as easy as it is advertised to be. Very few scientists have an instinct for crucial experiments. Most scientists engaged in research spend many of their hours in frustration. A creative scientist must be able to absorb almost endless punishment in order to achieve even minor insights. Even so, the competition is keen. To avoid being outdistanced, a scientist must be single-minded in his devotion to research and to the necessary reading of scientific journals. Small wonder that many give up the effort. Some who do so find opportunities in the administration of research.

Most, though not all, scientists who choose to become administrators are in effect admitting either some kind of lack of competence in research or an inability to abide with the discipline and disappointment of research. Or they are indicating a value system that places the satisfactions of authority above the zest for knowledge. Often the decision involves all three factors.

After a man becomes a full-time administrator, he is likely to be most comfortable with other administrators and politicians. The sympathies of the scientist-administrators lie with the research workers, and they conscientiously try to defend basic research against inroads by politicians. However, very soon after a man ceases to be active in creative work, his real contact with science atrophies. The conversation of the typical Washington science administrator revolves around the politics of science; rarely does it touch the content of science. After a short tenure as a full-time administrator, the one-time scientist is more closely attuned to the politicians than to the working scientists. He soon loses acuity of judgment in scientific matters. Moreover, Congress and the administration are on the scene and make their presence felt in many ways. The creative scientist is far away and immersed in his work.

The administrators attempt to broaden their base in science by consulting advisory committess. At all levels of government such groups are employed. At the higher levels, however, committee members are often only nominally connected with creative science.

As an aftermath of the first Sputnik, succeeding presidents have leaned on presidential science advisers, who at times have wielded a good deal of influence while in turn drawing on the advice of a rather narrow group of scientist authorities. When problems arise in other parts of the federal establishment, special advisory panels are assembled. These too consist of authorities. In the multiplicity of committees there is a tendency to employ a limited group of experts, so that the same people appear again and again. This oligarchy is at least as closely attuned to the art of the possible as to the search for truth. At its interface with politics, science is often a servant of authoritarianism.

I have served on a number of advisory committees and have noted considerable variability in their performance, depending on the type of problem under consideration. I have seen superb performance and many new ideas arising from committees considering technical problems. This occurred when the fund of knowledge made available by briefings and already resident in the group was sufficient to permit questions to be answered on a creative scientific basis. All too often, however, committees are asked to furnish judgments either in areas in which they are not fully competent or in areas in which no one answer is very good.

As long as committees are discussing scientific facts or hypotheses, they tend to behave objectively and democratically. When imponderables are considered, the atmosphere is more authoritarian. One or two of the more influential members tend to dominate the decisions.

Advisory groups seem most at sea when asked to consider how much money should be devoted to a given area of science — for example, high-energy physics. I sat on such a committee. A variety of approaches was employed. As a warm-up exercise, the group considered how big a machine might be constructed if the entire gross national product were devoted to it. The committee settled down to a long period of trying to guess how much money Congress might be induced to spend. Had this number been ascertainable, the committee could have decided very quickly how much to recommend.

Washington and science administration have a strong fascination to out-of-town scientists. Almost any scientist will drop what he is doing to go to Washington to sit on a committee. This willingness is often exploited. If a federal agency has a problem that seems too hot to handle, arrangements can be made to recruit a committee of distinguished bagholders. With proper selection, a cooperative group can be assembled. Usually the executive secretaries of such committees are government personnel. Since they prepare the agenda and write the minutes of the meeting, a suitable final outcome of the committee's effort can be arranged.

At lower levels of policy making — for instance, in the panels that advise on grants — the advisers are generally much closer to creative science. Also, usually their advice is honestly employed. But the government staff is again in position to implement its own prejudices and to exert very great influence in subtle ways.

The mechanism by which authoritarianism influences and shapes science in the United States is the control of funds. No single person is today in control, though at times individuals have come close to being czars. Federal shaping of this nation's research represents a composite summation of a number of programs. As a result, some areas of science are richly supported (space, for example, and molecular biology), while others, such as chemistry, are starved.

Adequate financial support for basic research in chemistry in universities[5] should enjoy a very high priority among the

[5]Adapted from an editorial by Philip H. Abelson entitled "Chemistry in the universities," *Science*, Vol. 144, No. 3616, p. 251, April 17, 1964.

federal granting agencies. Chemistry is crucial to science and technology alike. Advances in most sciences are dependent both on superior chemical techniques and on new fundamental understanding of matter and its reactions. Chemistry is central to many fields, among them biochemistry, molecular biology, neurochemistry, chemotaxonomy, and solid-state physics.

Advances in pure chemistry are prerequisites to progress in applied chemistry, including such fields as polymers, petrochemicals, and chemotherapeutics.

During the last decade chemistry has been out of the spotlight as attention has been focused on atomic energy, electronics, and space. In all these activities science has had an important though not always clearly identifiable role. Over the long haul the strongest nation will be the one that applies chemistry most effectively. The long-range interests of our nation require a strong chemical profession, and basic to this are strong chemistry departments in the universities.

Until recently the need for federal support in chemistry was urgent but not acute. Costs of supplies and equipment were comparatively modest. That is no longer true. The style of chemical research has changed. Today's well-equipped laboratory is a maze of electronic gear. The need for modern instruments and equipment in university chemistry laboratories is now critical.

In the light of the importance of chemistry and the number of students being trained, a substantial fraction of the total support for basic research should go to chemistry. But this does not happen. During fiscal 1963, total government support of basic research in chemistry in universities amounted to about $38 million. In the same period the space agency was providing more than $500 million for research in space and another $3.2 billion for development work. In fiscal 1964, support for chemistry increased only slightly while support for NASA increased more than 30 per cent. This disparate treatment of the essential and the glamorous points up a weakness in federal funding of research. Why has space, which is of limited importance, fared so much better than chemistry, which is fundamental? The answer is that space is spectacular. Science administrators and scientist-politicians know that Congress will respond to spectaculars but that it is cool to the solid, painstaking work that, small step by small step, builds lasting science.

By providing large sums for some activities and relatively less for others, Congress and the granting agencies are shaping science in this country. There is little evidence that anyone has considered the effects of these actions. Perhaps that is fortunate. If the power inherent in federal funding of research were exploited, the situation could be very bad. Indeed, a principal reason why the federal grants system works reasonably well is that it is not highly organized. In many fields several agencies are involved, and the diversity acts against the creation of petty czars in many branches of science.

Perhaps authority is exerting the greatest influence in curtailing free speech among scientists. As far as I know, neither science administrators nor the Congress has sought this outcome. It has developed inevitably out of the fact that universities are now heavily dependent on government funds. No one wishes to take a chance on incurring the wrath of a group that could enforce crippling sanctions. Discovery of the depth of self-imposed censorship came to me only after I became editor of *Science*. Since that time I have written an occasional editorial critical of Congress or science administrators. As a result I have been approached by scores of scientists who have warned me that my actions were hazardous. I have been therefore on the alert to note attitudes of scientists in their relations to the government. Galileo would be ashamed at the bland way in which his intellectual progeny avoid controversy. This lack of character could have serious consequences not only to science but also to the nation as a whole. As an example, consider the $5 billion space program. The House and Senate committees heard extensive testimony from government witnesses representing, for example, the National Aeronautics and Space Administration.[6] Although a majority of the nation's scientists question facets of the program, no opposing witnesses appeared. In part, this was because they were not invited; in part, because they did not seek a hearing.

There are several reasons why scientists do not try to testify at hearings on research and development legislation. Most scientists are unaware of the schedule of impending hearings and unfamiliar with mechanisms for obtaining an audience. Only a limited number feel competent to make judgments in the diverse, highly technical areas. With few exceptions there are no staffs to aid in preparation of material. A major reason why research and development legislation is not more adequately discussed is a lack of, or evident immediate clash of, self-interest among scientists. The self-interest of those who advocate expenditures is obvious, but who makes the probing counterargument?

Failure of scientists to criticize publicly programs that many consider ill judged often stems from analysis of the balance sheet of their own self-interest. On the one side is the consideration that the long-term interest of their pro-

[6]Adapted from an editorial by Philip H. Abelson entitled "Only one side of the question," *Science*, Vol. 145, No. 3630, p. 347, July 24, 1964.

fession and the nation dictates that unwise expenditures not be made. If the public loses confidence in the integrity of scientists, the sequel could be harmful for all. But this is a nebulous possibility that does not outweigh the realities of the present. In questioning the wisdom of the establishment the witness pays a price and incurs hazards. He is diverted from his professional activities. He stirs the enmity of powerful foes. He fears that reprisals may extend beyond him to his institution. Perhaps his fears are shadows, but, in a day when almost all research institutions are highly dependent on federal funds, prudence seems to dictate silence.

I have outlined a situation in which the forces of authority have gained advantages in the conflict with those who follow the principles of Galileo. But let us not spend too much time mourning the good old days. Authoritarianism has always been with us. It always will be. We would do well to analyze the situation and attempt to be constructive. What is at stake in this conflict? Should society concern itself with science versus authoritarianism? How can we prevent its gaining further domination over science? How can we minimize its effects on the work of scientists? Important aspects of the future of our civilization depend on this struggle. Economic, military, and spiritual issues are at stake. It should not be necessary to emphasize the role science has played as a foundation on which to build a complex technology, and I shall not labor the point. We tend, however, to lose sight of the values of science in less material fields. Today most of the earthly land frontiers have been explored.[7] Where can society look for innovation?

[7]Adapted from an editorial by Philip H. Abelson entitled "Science in the new political climate," *Science*, Vol. 146, No. 3642, p. 345, October 16, 1964.

For new challenges? We must change continuously, or we stagnate. Among our best sources of innovation are science and technology. Keeping science free of authoritarianism is essential, for the spirit of science is innovation. One other value of science has not been much discussed of late. It springs from man's hunger to know. Even today we are faced with many unknowns. They represent an invigorating challenge to man and to science. When science thrusts back the frontiers of ignorance, it does so for all men, and all men can enjoy a greater sense of the dignity of man for it.

Society, then, has a stake in the conflict for authoritarianism can cripple science. On a national scale we have the example of the Soviet Union. The success of Sputnik may blind some to the effectiveness of Soviet science, but a detailed examination indicates that along with strengths in some areas go gaps and serious weaknesses in others. In the practical sphere an example is the Russian performance in the field of plastics. They have recently signed a contract to import a plant from England. The Lysenko affair in genetics is one of the more unsavory episodes in science anywhere. We have also observed the effects of authority on a more limited scale. At long last the German universities are acting to limit the privileges of their authoritarian Herren Professoren. All scientists have seen around them examples of authority being in error in attempting to dictate research programs.

A crucial problem in safeguarding science is to find a means of financing research without subjecting it to the wrong kind of controls. At the same time we should not adopt the fuzzy-minded approach that scientists should be supported without any checks or restraints. At the very least we must remember that federal funds have to be managed responsibly and must be accounted for.

If we reflect on the conflict of science and authority, we can see that the danger comes not from mere authority but from monolithic authority. In some fields of research in which the federal government furnishes most of the money, there is no present problem. Funds are available from several different granting agencies. No single individual is in a position to dictate who or what gets supported. Other areas are not quite so fortunate — chemistry, for instance. Sufficient funds have not been provided. Looking ahead we can see that powerful congressmen, especially members of the appropriations committee, could if they chose blackball almost any area of science, particularly those that sound esoteric. Moreover, Congress could move toward eliminating the multiple-agency approach. A favorite target is waste and duplication. It could easily be argued that allowing two agencies to provide grants in the same area of science is wasteful duplication. Furthermore, there has been persistent talk about establishing a single department of science. Presumably this would diminish duplication and thus bring on the worst consequences of authoritarianism in government funding.

The best reply to present dependence on federal funds for research would be the development of alternative sources. For example, if the states were to assume only a moderate fraction of the burden, the situation would be much sounder. Even were the present dependence on federal funds to continue, the methods of allotment could be improved. I believe that a substantial part of federal research funds, for example, 25 per cent, should be given directly to the universities, the university administrations to be responsible for their proper and wise expenditure.

Such a move would not bring on universal Utopia. In a few universities distribution of the funds would be governed by petty tyrants or by logrolling. But diversity of judgment would be greatly increased, and, in at least some universities, the quality of administration would be brilliantly superior to anything Washington could offer. Indeed, we can safely predict that out of this diversity would arise new and superior methods of allocating money for basic research in this country.

Direct allocation of funds to universities could help correct some present imbalances in distribution. Some steps in this direction must be taken to avoid the calamity of making research funds part of an out-and-out pork barrel.

Over the long pull, perhaps our greatest problem is not merely money; it is courage. We must create conditions under which at least a few of our scientists will feel free to question the wisdom of authority.

I would suggest that it is of the utmost importance that we achieve in this country a new revolutionary development. We must establish a situation in which at least a few first-class universities carry on excellent research while taking not one cent from the government. Were this achieved, it would not be surprising if the faculties of these establishments quickly became the elite of science and the envy of the academic world.

Today, all of us are indebted to Galileo and the patterns he established, but we too can make lasting contributions to mankind. We need only exhibit a small fraction of the courage and diligence he displayed for our lives to count positively in the continuing conflict between science and authority.

6

ERICH KAHLER

SCIENCE AND HISTORY

Let us start with a fundamental question: What is all our knowledge for, what is, or should be, the aim of our striving for ever more and more knowledge? It is good, indeed necessary, to ask this question from time to time lest we forget about the ultimate end of our intellectual endeavors. Our intellectual activities have become so institutionalized and compartmentalized, the problems in which we are involved have grown so overwhelmingly complex and besetting that we are apt to lose sight of this guiding aim.

Let us go back to the dim origins. What was the initial urge that stimulated man to seek knowledge? The question takes us to the primeval stage of man in which what may be called instinct passes over into conscious attempt. The borderlines are fluid, but we may learn something from the observation of an infant, and a little child, trying gradually to cope with his surroundings. The apparently aimless first movements, the groping of the little hands, the wondering eyes eager to take in what happens around them, all this betrays the rudimentary urge of the human being to get to know his environment, to learn how to deal with it. The playing of the child, likewise, is a very serious affair, very different from the adult's playing; it is the continuation, within a somewhat broader scope, of the groping of the infant; it is a kind of training, with quasi-experimental objects and objectives, for the mastery of his world. And so it goes on in the life of the adult, in the life of man, the desire at the same time to orient himself in his environment, to learn how to deal with it, and to put it to use. Curiosity, which is often referred to as the ultimate motive of man's drive toward knowledge, is by no means the original incentive. Curiosity is a by-product of the need of orientation, of man's need for self-maintenance and self-expansion, a by-product which developed rather late into a dominant motive, a kind of *l' art pour l'art* of knowledge, when means became self-contained ends. The range of man's self-expansion widened more and more in the course of fighting, exploring, and exploiting his environment, until the conceptual task came to exceed the individual's capacities and called for collective efforts, for instruments and methods of abstractest concentration. But, in all our absorbing explorations at the remotest frontiers, we should keep aware of the original and ultimate end of these endeavors, and that is the maintenance of humanity, of the human being. When man has reached the stage where world religion and the very achievements of science have taught him, or should have taught him, the natural equality of human rights, that is, what I would call the *identity of man*, it is no longer the human individual or any group of individuals that has to be maintained but humanity, the human form and dignity.

We live today in a scientistic, more and more scientified world, a world dominated by science, its principles and methods, and its application, which is technology. This does not mean, I hasten to say, that human beings, the majority of people, act according to the principle of science, which would mean that they make their decisions more rationally than before. On the contrary, I am afraid, as far as the conduct of human life is concerned, people are to-day particularly prone to irrational acts. This is precisely the result of, and overcompensation for, that functional over-rationalization — mechanization, quantification, organization, bureaucratization — which is the inevitable consequence of the progress of science and technology and of the more and more intricate task of regulating the public concerns of a rapidly increasing population and life machinery. People feel their personal lives narrowed in by this vast network of collective control, organizational and scientifico-technocratical, and they do not see why this has to be and how this hangs together. They are inclined irrationally to cut through the complexities, which they are incapable of understanding, and to restore conditions as they existed before the recent world-shaking advances in science and technology, before the inherent technical interdependence of people and peoples all over the globe.

This is the extremely dangerous situation in which we find ourselves today. The psychic and mental condition of individuals did not keep pace with the speed of collective functional achievements. People have lost their bearings in their world, they are motivated by the expediencies of the moment and of their parochial wants. And this means that they have lost their sense of history, their sense of the evolution of human conditions.

It will be no news to anyone watchful of present trends when I say that ours is an antihistorical, antievolutional era. There is, to be sure, much official talk of progress, but what is meant by progress in such talk is the advancement of functional achievements in science and technology. Certainly, it includes social care and legislation, but this is precisely what is opposed by large sections of our population. There is hardly an awareness of the fact that those scientific and technological achievements have a bearing on social conditions. People want to enjoy the advantages and comforts of our increased knowledge and technical skills but refuse to accept the social consequences. However, in the very methods of their opposition, they cannot help being subject to the influence of the organizational techniques of our time.

So far I have spoken of the people at large. But antihistorism, antievolutionism has also taken hold of considerable parts of our intellectual and academic community. This has two main reasons: The first is the result of our experiences since the First World War that have utterly discredited belief in human progress, that is to say, in human betterment and increase of happiness. We have seen civilizations crumble and revert to extreme barbarism, humanitarian treaties and charters reneged, and unheard-of atrocities committed by peoples that had arrived at the highest cultural standard. And the follies and frenzies, the anxieties and frustrations that multiply with the inventions of our gadgetries and weaponries, with the whole mechanized apparatus of our life, do not fit exactly into the image of human happiness that our progress-minded forefathers in the eighteenth and nineteenth centuries had cherished. And since the idea of progress and the concept of human evolution had developed together, and were seen as one and the same process, the concept of human evolution broke down together with the concept of progress. This, in conjunction with the confusing overgrowth of uncovered historical details, resulted not only in a denial of history as a consistent development of man, but also in a rejection of the historical viewpoint as a means to explain human conditions and problems. I quote one prominent historian for many,

Geoffrey Barraclough, who writes: "We ourselves have experienced enough of discontinuity to feel renewed sympathy with all those historians who, from the time of Augustine and Orosius, have been more impressed by the cataclysmic than by the continuous in human affairs . . . no present-day issue is, or ever was, intelligible in terms of its history."

But the disbelief in historical evolution is not the only motivation for our present antihistorism. There is another one, connected with the first, and, I would think, even more powerful. It has to do precisely with the overwhelming influence of science and the scientific point of view on our whole life, and so on all our intellectual activities. The predominance of the cyclic view of history, as it is expressed in recent theories, such as those of Spengler, Toynbee, and Sorokin, involves in itself a scientific approach, tending as it does to the search for historical "laws of nature." Not to speak of the typological and taxonomic treatment of history prevailing in modern sociology — think of Max Weber's "ideal types," and of the statistical methods of American sociology, and American, and not only American, anthropology (in Europe Lévi-Strauss versus Lévy-Bruhl).

Now here we are at the crucial point: the relation between science and history, which I would characterize as a fundamental difference in their premises and their subject matter, a difference that calls for diametrically opposite methods of approach.

To be sure, most historians have come to realize that history is not a science. History, it is argued, has to do with a motley multitude and multiformity of singular phenomena — happenings, conditions, personalities, nations — that cannot be subsumed under general laws. And from the standpoint of science, Professor Karl Popper in his book,

The Poverty of Historicism, supports this view by stating that history is neither amenable to verification through experiments nor to quantification of methods of research. He refers to such features of history as novelty, complexity, unpredictability, unavoidable selectivity of presentation, insufficiency of causal explanation, all precluding scientific treatment.

We seem confronted with a choice between two antagonistic notions: On the one hand, history is seen as a chaotic medley of the most diverse entities and occurrences, in which it is impossible to discern any order and regularity; indeed historians, just as the general public, appear to derive a real pleasure from the unrestrained imagination of the "fortuitous and unforeseen," the discontinuous, the "cataclysmic" — to quote Barraclough again — a delight in "the most exhilarating testimony to the creative vigour, the splendid variety, of the human spirit." On the other hand, we have the strained, quasi-scientific "laws of history," as propounded by theorists of history.

I for one am inclined to reject both of these views of history, which reflect, in the intellectual domain, the current popular divergence of overrationalization and irrationalism. I cannot bring myself to recognize a scientistic regularity of historical processes, as it is suggested by the theorists of history; nor do I find it possible to agree with historians to whom history is devoid of any kind of intelligible order and just an intrinsically incoherent sequence of circumstantial events and human inventions. In the following brief outline I will attempt to show what appears to me the true nature of history and the basic difference between the scientific outlook and an approach accordant with the distinctive character of historical reality.

The methods of science are based on the assumption of

the *immutable stability of nature,* an assumption which, paradoxically enough, is a religious heritage. It originated in the concept of a cosmic order created once and for all by the will of God. Even for Newton the laws of nature were laws ordained by God, and the study of the universe was identical with the study of God's creation. In the course of ever more elaborate research the image of God gradually vanished into a more and more distant background, but the belief in the stability of nature remained. Since the innovations of the Ockhamist school in the fourteenth century, this belief began to be shaken in a restricted domain — Galileo's famous conflict with the Church brought this into the open — and the whole history of astronomy, physics, and biology in the modern period may be seen as a history of an increasing erosion of the concept of the stability of nature.

The decisive pushes began at the end of the eighteenth century with the rise of the biological evolution theory. A succession of great scientists, from Buffon and Cuvier to Geoffrey Saint-Hilaire, Lamarck, and Darwin overcame, against powerful traditional resistance, the old method of mere classification of divinely created beings. These scientists gradually realized the autonomous and consistent development of living forms, and this very discovery opened the way to a true, and ever deeper, understanding of organic structures and functions. To be sure, an element of stability persisted in the search for a static regularity of genetic processes. But recently, even the absolute validity of Mendelism seems to be questioned.

In physics, a corresponding development has taken place. Faraday's study of electromagnetic "forces of matter" eventually led to the modern field concept. Maxwell's theory of electromagnetic phenomena was the starting point of the theory of relativity and its invalidation of absolute space and time. The development was quickened by Becquerel's and the Curies' discovery of radioactive spontaneous disintegration of matter and Rutherford's transformation of chemical elements — the "element" has long ceased to be elementary. Finally, Einstein's famous formula, which equates matter and energy, means the dissolution of the old "material" matter. Nuclear physics as well as recent astronomy shows nature as a process, in particular and in general. Astronomy has become a historical discipline.

So, at the frontiers of our presently known universe, the spheres of the particles and of the cosmic bodies, the concept of nature's stability is shaken. This has altered the character of fact, it has restricted the validity of causality. Such modifications show a certain approximation of scientific views to what I will presently try to set forth as the essentially historical approach and method. But a fundamental difference remains, and will remain, in spite of our new experience of the dynamic character of nature, a difference which is founded on an insuperable difference of human perspective. To be sure, the advancing research in various fields of science has discovered irregularities and uncertainties which have created serious theoretical problems and caused modifications like the replacement, in specific domains, of strict laws by statistical laws. But such irregularities occur in regions so remote from the reach of our human, immediate perception and practical uses, they are so minute or so huge in relation to human proportions, that they are practically insignificant and may be disregarded. Not only are the laws of classical mechanics still valid for large bodies, not only do statistical laws suffice for a safe practical application even of nuclear forces, but the dimensions of the entities and movements with which our physical research has to deal are such that they cannot be approached by other than quantifying means. Only equal entities or processes can be subjected to quantification. Although some crazy people have gone as far as to attribute free will to particles, it remains unquestionable that individual differences on this level have not reached a degree relevant for the study and application of physical phenomena. A short-lived cell in my body, if it were endowed with consciousness, would probably perceive and count on only the seemingly perennial, and thus predictable and quantifiable, regularities in the body — breathing, heartbeat, metabolism, and so forth — but hardly be aware of the major moves and changes on the higher level of the organism, let alone the psychic motions of the person. This otherwise incommensurable, almost metaphorical, example is of course meant only to illustrate the distances between human and cosmic proportions and the limitation of human perspective, which will forever compel science in its exploratory ventures to use the methods of quantification and an ever more concentrated abstraction. So, just as the realization of biological evolution did not prevent biology from using quantitative methods when it came to delve into the depths of genetics, in the same way physics will have to stick to its methods of high-powered abstraction, which actually presuppose the absolute validity of laws and causality. Science will continue to proceed *as if* nature were stable.

The essentially human world, however, which started not with the highest apes, the *proconsulidae*, nor even with *pithecanthropus erectus*, that is to say, with man's physical development, but with history — and that means the evolution of consciousness — this world is fully noticeable in our own familiar dimensions. While nature *itself* — not our *concepts* of nature — has remained rather much the same for us since the inception of human times, our human world, the nature of man's close environment, his ways of life, indeed to a certain degree man himself, have changed enormously. We undergo directly, indeed we actively participate, in these changes, and our experiences can teach us to realize the interaction between man and nature and the perpetual interaction between man's concepts and man's action, between his ever-widening scope of consciousness and his ever-expanding range of operations and groupings. *This is, in fact, what constitutes history: the interaction, intercreation of conceptuality and actuality, of consciousness and action.* History is not only what we have learned in school, a succession of wars and treaties, conquests and defeats, powers and civilizations, social and technological conditions, it is essentially not that medley of nations, personalities, popular and intellectual movements; it is above all the evolution of a unique, organic genus, the evolution of man, of which all the politicial, social, and intellectual happenings are just the manifestations and vehicles. And, being the evolution of man, history does not represent a repository of a dead past: History is something that stays and lives with us in every moment of our lives, that inheres in all our acts and projects, something whose very result we all are. When we study history, we have to be constantly aware of the fact that we are studying the life and career of the *genus humanum.*

History has the appearance of an incoherent variety of power struggles, cultural trends, and personal creations only when we see it proceeding on a single plane, when we see it *planimetrically,* as it were. There are, however, various levels of history, as there are diverse levels of all reality. All of us live at the same time on different levels of existence. There is a physical level, and on that level I am, with regard to my subordinate cells and organs, a genus and generality. There is the level of the person, on which I am, with regard to the superior entity, the community or collective to which I belong, an individual. There is the level of communities and collectives, of families, nations, states, professions, and so forth, which in turn are, in relation to the *genus humanum*, particular, individual entities. These levels imply different extents of existential scope. When we compare the range of existence of the physical being, the animal, or the human being as animal, with the scope of the completed person and his consciousness — or the range of a primitive clan with the range of a nation and its cultural and civilizational implications — not only the existential differences but also the evolutional coherence of history will become evident. Of course, we can notice these differences and these evolutional changes only when we clearly distinguish the different levels of history, when we conceive of history not as "world history," or as "history of mankind," which would mean the history of the sum total of human individuals, but as the evolution of the *genus humanum*. History is not, as a positivistic view has it, a sum total of the acts, experiences, and feelings of all the millions of private individuals who ever existed on earth. The course of history takes place, and can be seen clearly, only on the communal level, and not on the level of the private individual, whose mode of existence derives mainly from the state of his communal civilization.

The disregard of the differences of historical levels is due to the predominance of the scientific requirement of sensory verification. For science the validity of concepts or assumptions is established only if it is verified, however deviously, instrumentally, by sensory perception. The senses are the ultimate instance — the very word "evidence" expresses it.

Science itself recognizes different levels of nature: to put them roughly, the level of particles, of nuclei, of atoms, of molecules and macromolecules, of chromosomes, of cells, of organs, of organisms; and different sciences concern themselves with the respective phenomena of these different levels: physics, chemistry, biochemistry, biology, histology, anatomy and physiology, and so forth. Nobody questions the existence of such different levels and evolutionary stages of nature because their phenomena can be reached by our senses. But such clear distinction stops at the threshold of history, since no strict sensory perception and verification of entities beyond the individual is possible. And yet, the actual unfolding of levels and stages did not cease at the inception of history, it went on, actually and conceptually, that is, in the course of sociopolitical processes and of the concomitant evolution of consciousness. Since these levels and stages are not perceptible and verifiable by our senses, they are not validated by a scientistic view of history. Until the beginning of our century, scientists were inclined to trace back the phenomena of higher levels to those of lower and ultimately the lowest level, to reduce, for instance, organic structures and processes to physicochemical mechanisms. More recently, scientists, while not denying, indeed even more deeply understanding, the connections among the different levels — the borderlines between inorganic matter and life appear to have almost vanished — nevertheless came to recognize the specifically novel characteristics arising with every shift from one level to another.

Because of this, as I would call it, *vertical division* of nature into the different levels of physical reality, a division that has determined the order of specialization of scientific disciplines, science was enabled to preserve an over-all structure of its picture of the universe. The different levels of physical reality are, and will remain, recognized as different stages of evolution. We are about to learn the formation of life out of inorganic matter. We know the main lines of the evolution of the earth and of living forms up to the physical completion of the human form, and, because of this structural and evolutional order that science has preserved, it has still, highly specialized as it is, fulfilled the task of man's orientation in his extrahuman world. Conversely, the humanistic disciplines, those concerned with specifically human matters, with psychic, intellectual, cultural, social, political affairs, have developed a rather *horizontal division* into the different fields of activity and expression of the human being. Thereby, in the course of rigid specialization, the sense of an organic coherence of human faculties, indeed of human existence, was lost. Up to the beginning of the nineteenth century, this sense of organic coherence of human life and of human evolution was still prevalent; the belief in progress and the corresponding study of biological evolution kept it alive. But the increasing influence of scientistic analysis of quasi-stable phenomena, in conjunction with the crumbling of the idea of progress, discredited the concept of human evolution, or at least shoved it into the background. The specialization of humanistic scholarship took the form of studies of the various human functions, activities, and modes of expression: language, epistemological and logical relations, arts, religion, psychic, social, political, economic conditions, and so forth, with their specifically functional developments. Among all these functional sections of scholarship, history has been given its restricted place as a study of past happenings, political and cultural. As a result of such horizontal division of humanistic scholarship into partly stabilized, partly functionalized sections of human life and of the disregard of human evolution, history as a whole assumed the aspect of a muddle of "discontinuous," "irreducibly particular" phenomena and lost its capacity to afford people an orientation in their immediate, human environment and a guidance in the conduct of human affairs. A general direction of conduct may be derived only from a *stereoscopic* view of history; that is, a view of history as a consistent evolution of man, which proceeds on different levels, in different dimensions, and in different stages, whereby the different evolutional stages coincide with a shift from one level to another. A first, prehistoric shift from a lower to a next higher level may be seen in the transition from the animal to the human being, which means the transition from a predominantly physical, instinctually guided being to a predominantly conscious, mentally directed being. And the most recent shift, which started with the revolutions at the end of the eighteenth century and whose completion we have witnessed in our own lifetime, is the passing over from the plane of individuality to that of collectivity; from a stage where the individual predominated in the course of events to a stage where the point of gravity shifted to the prevalence of masses, teams, and organizations, and where immediate action has turned decisively into instrumental action.

These shifts are connected with, indeed they are a manifestation of, a gradual expansion of existential scope, expanse of the determinant units of history, and expanse of the reach of human consciousness. On the sociopolitical plane this evolution — not to be confounded with progress, which has a value connotation — proceeds from the theocratic temple-city to the city and city-state, settling down here below as a mundane community — even the Roman Empire was still a city-state; then, through the intermediary of feudal principalities, which were the first to give the non-urban territory some political weight, to the territorial estate; from the territorial estate to the dynastical and nation-state; from the nation-state to the fully developed nation, representing the whole of the people; from the nation to the civilizational and ideological power bloc, comprising a whole continent or even intercontinental unit; and finally to the technical, technological prefiguration of a "one world," which is psychologically very far from realization, but which looms as the only alternative that science and technology have presented us to their opposite achievement, nuclear or biochemical annihilation.

There is no need to dwell more elaborately on the counterpart — the vast extension of human consciousness, which was alternately the carrier and the result of the sociopolitical expansion. The advances of theoretical and applied science into remotest cosmic reaches and into innermost depths of organic structures are obvious enough. Knowledge, conceptuality, is awareness. Unfortunately, but inevitably, this growing human awareness, having become institutionalized, has outgrown the capacity of individual consciousness. The corpus of this ever-advancing human knowledge, of this ever-expanding human awareness of spheres and relations never exposed before, the totality of these "knowns," not knowable by any single person alive, constitutes a kind of *collective consciousness*, which is, as I indicated before, as much of a danger as it is an attainment.

I characterized history as the evolution of man, consisting in an expanding interaction, intercreation of human structures and human consciousness, of actuality and conceptuality. Since history is perceptible, indeed experienced life-size, as it were, directly in our own human sphere, in the entirety of its movements, we are able to observe in it a *complete reality,* which is a blend of change and continuity, of particularity and generality. To be sure, to a certain extent features and modes of process repeat themselves in the course of history. So there exists a degree of scientistic regularity also in history. But these historical regularities are inextricably fused with particularities; we cannot neatly separate generalities from particularities in history. The diversities are looming too strongly. And therefore it is impossible and fallacious to try to establish "laws of history" comparable to scientific "laws of nature." In extra-human nature — which comprises the purely physical aspect of human nature — we are able to isolate regularities, probably because of the disproportionate distances, temporal and spatial, which prevent us from a perception of its complete reality. We are forever condemned to apprehend only a *partial reality* of nature. In history, our own, codimensional sphere, isolation of generalities will always appear strained and inadequate, and historians are inclined to react to their insufficiencies by holding history to consist solely of particularities and contending that, as a whole, history lacks any kind of order. Thus they are apt to disregard the specific order inherent in history.

This specific order of historical happening seems to me to consist in the *expansive evolution,* which I have tried to indicate, and in the *distinctive levels of existence* that mark the steps of this evolution. A coherence of development can be demonstrated in the course of history, and the historical equivalent of the strictness of scientific laws may be seen in the rigor of this coherence. To make myself somewhat clearer on this point, I have to add a few remarks concerning the meaning of fact and causality in history, as compared with their significance for science.

Fact and causality are intrinsically related: Causality con-

nects fact with fact. Facts, therefore, to be fit for a causal nexus, have to be firmly established and sharply defined, indeed *confined*. And this is possible only in a static, stabilized order. In a dynamic order, such as the closely observable coherence of historical evolution, both sharply delimitable facts and strict causality break down. To be sure, in history, too, we have distinctly delimitable facts. It can be established, for instance, when a person was born and when he died, when a battle was fought, or a treaty was concluded. But such firmly established historical data have a role and character very different from their equivalents in science. They stand alone, causally unrelated to each other, and, due to this lack of relatedness, they explain nothing. They become relevant merely through connections with facts of an entirely different kind, facts that do not stand solidly by themselves, but exist only in combinations, in groups, clusters, chains, of phenomena, in which they merge. And this is why they require that so-much-deplored selection and interpretation, a selection and interpretation that could derive a criterion of validity only from a vantage point on a level higher and broader than the one of the observed and described phenomena. So, in trying to understand history, we are again led from level to level.

Let us take as an example the French Revolution, which Professor Barraclough would certainly not hesitate to regard as a cataclysmic event of the first order, in which, as he says, the new, "the fortuitous and the unforeseen . . . breaks through untrammeled by the past." Now the French Revolution, a real turning point if ever there was one, was, in point of fact, long in coming and had its origins in a vast variety of places, movements, and levels. I cannot and need not in our context detail the story of these preparations, which have been thoroughly explored and described by

great scholars. I just want to recall for our purpose what multitude of preliminaries and preconditions led up to the final event. In the religious domain the process of secularization was well advanced even since the end of the Middle Ages. The Calvinist reform, with its presbyterian and congregational constitutions, had gotten into conflict with the monarchical principle. Its political effects were manifest in the Huguenot wars and in the decisive influence of the Levellers on the English Revolution. Politically, the French Revolution was preceded by the liberation of the Netherlands, the English Revolution, which set the example of a popular execution of a king, and, shortly before the French, the American Revolution, whose impact on the European minds cannot be overrated. When we look at the social and economic situation, we find that the French government had been bankrupt practically since Louis XIV, and the attempts of Colbert, Vauban, Turgot, and Necker to persuade the kings to a new economic policy appropriate to the trend of the time were abortive because of the political and social changes it involved. The peasants, whose personal services had been almost completely converted into taxes, were susceptible to revolutionary demands, precisely because they were no longer as desperately downtrodden as to be incapable of imagining an improvement of their condition. The middle class had grown wealthy enough to feel hampered by governmental restrictions on commercial enterprise and to be stirred by the example of the British industrialists, who had just begun to subvert the old guild regulations. In the nobility, a mood of ennui, of self-weariness and slackening self-assurance had taken effect, which opened their minds to the revolutionary ideas of Rousseau, of the Physiocrats, and the Encyclopedists. Materialistic philosophy had spread, and technological innovations had

fostered the belief in progress. All such developments were reflected in, and reactively promoted by, the arts.

Now this is of course a very sketchy picture of the pre-revolutionary situation. Every single determinant that I listed represents a whole complex of motives and preliminary processes. When we look more closely into the situation we shall find it impossible to set apart, and add up, single causes of the final event. Not only are they innumerable, but they pass into one another, act upon one another, and, in scrutinizing the elements of this whole assemblage of preconditions, we are carried farther and farther, through an unending genealogy of processes, into the most diverse, spatially and temporally remote scenes of happenings. We are led to consider the political, economic, and intellectual developments in the Netherlands, England, and America. We shall be taken back, through a progressive consecution of philosophical theories and techniques, to the sources of rationalism and empiricism, to the transformations of the concept of natural law; to Descartes, to Galileo and Copernicus, indeed the Middle Ages. This again is a random selection. The study of the progression of the revolution itself will draw us into an investigation of the dynastic and feudal mentality and of the counterrevolutionary invasions, which always help to radicalize revolutionary processes, and finally into the background and the psychology of the leading personalities.

The French Revolution was an exemplary turning point in history, inaugurating a shift from one level to another. But in this truly revolutionary event hardly anything appears fortuitous or discontinuous, and what makes it cataclysmic is just the ripeness of the moment, the simultaneous conjunction of the results of long-grown forces and circumstances. History is growth, an all-out continual process, and in it causation is limitless and endless. It is futile to ask *why* something happened, it carries you to the beginning of time. There is no *prima causa*. The only fruitful question is *how* things happened. Wherever we take up a historical investigation, the search for the how may lead us deeper into the understanding of the working of the historical process, if only we keep in mind the distinction of stages, levels, and dimensions of history.

What these observations were meant to suggest is that any historical research, be it ever so specialized, should be done with an awareness of the distinctive character of history and of the ultimate aim of historical studies. We need a new view of history, keeping clear of the two extreme positions that seem predominantly held today: the emulation of science and the denial of any consistency and evolutional order of history. We need it in order to recover some orientation and guidance in our badly disrupted human world.

INDEX

Index

Index

Index

Index